I am Kipper

Written by Roderick Hunt
Illustrated by Nick Schon,
based on the original characters
created by Roderick Hunt and Alex Brychta

OXFORD

UNIVERSITY PRESS

Read our names

Welcome to Read with Oxford

Featuring much-loved characters, great authors, engaging storylines and fun activities, **Read with Oxford** offers an exciting range of carefully levelled reading books to build your child's reading confidence.

From the very first steps in phonics all the way to reading independence, our unique and simple levelling system – **Read with Oxford Stages** – will guide you to choose the right book for your child.

For more information about **Read with Oxford Stages** and the whole range go to **oxfordowl.co.uk**. You'll also find lots of useful advice, free eBooks and activities to support your child through their learning journey.

Helping your child with phonics

Phonics is a way of teaching reading that is used in Primary schools. Children are taught to read letters or groups of letters by saying the sound(s) they represent; so they are taught the letter 'm' sounds like 'mmm' when we say it. Children are then taught more sounds, and learn to blend them to read words.

This book is part of the comprehensive and trusted range of support for learning at home from Oxford University Press.

You will find more advice and resources to support your child's learning on Oxford Owl. **oxfordowl.co.uk**.

Read with Oxford

Progress with Oxford

Bond – exam preparation

Dictionaries

Tips for reading *I am Kipper*

This book has two stories: *I am Kipper* (page 3) and *The Dog Tag* (page 17).

- Talk about the title and the picture on the front cover and title pages of each story.
- Find the letters *o* and *a* in these titles and talk about the sounds they make when you read these words.
- Look at the *o* and *a* words on pages 4 and 18. Say the sounds in each word and then say each word (e.g. *P-a-m, Pam*).
- Read the stories together and find the words with the letters *o* and *a* in them.
- Talk about the story.
- Do the fun activities at the end of each story.

Children enjoy re-reading stories and this helps to build their confidence.

Have fun!

After you have read *The Dog Tag*, find the five toy cats in the pictures.

The main sounds practised in this book are 'o' as in *dog* and 'a' as in *cat*.

For more activities, free eBooks and practical advice to help your child progress with reading visit **oxfordowl.co.uk**

I am Kipper.

I am Pam.

I am Mat.

I am Pat.

I am Tom.

I am Mac.

I am Sam.

Sam

Pat

Mat

Mac

Tom

Pam

12

Talk about the story

Where was Sam?

What was Pam doing?

What were the children dressed up as?

What kinds of games do you play with your friends?

13

Missing letters

Choose the letter to make the word.

h m p t

__op

__op

__ap

__op

Who did what?

Match each child with the right word.

tap

mop

hop

pop

The Dog Tag

Written by Roderick Hunt
Illustrated by Nick Schon,
based on the original characters
created by Roderick Hunt and Alex Brychta

OXFORD
UNIVERSITY PRESS

Read these words

got	cat
top	cap
pot	mat
mop	tag

Kipper got a cat.

Biff got a top.

Chip got a cap.

Mum got a pot.

Dad got a mop.

Floppy got a mat.

Floppy got a tag.

Floppy sat on the mat . . .

. . . and he got a pat.

Talk about the story

What did Kipper get?

What did Mum get?

Where were the family?

What would you like to get?

27

Missing letters

Choose the letter to finish the word.

ca___

ca___

mo___

ta___

Rhyming pairs

Say the words. Find pairs of words that rhyme.

top

mat

cat

mop

A maze

Help Kipper to get to Floppy.

OXFORD
UNIVERSITY PRESS

Great Clarendon Street, Oxford OX2 6DP

Oxford University Press is a department of the University of Oxford.
It furthers the University's objective of excellence in research, scholarship,
and education by publishing worldwide. Oxford is a registered trade mark
of Oxford University Press in the UK and in certain other countries

Text © Roderick Hunt 2007
Illustrations © Alex Brychta and Nick Schon 2007

First published 2007
This edition published 2020

Series Editors: Kate Ruttle, Annemarie Young

British Library Cataloguing in Publication Data available

ISBN: 978-0-19-277396-8

10 9 8 7 6 5 4 3 2

Printed in China

Paper used in the production of this book is a natural,
recyclable product made from wood grown in sustainable forests.
The manufacturing process conforms to the environmental
regulations of the country of origin.

I am Kipper is a **Read with Oxford Stage 1** book for children who are taking their first steps in reading. If your child enjoyed this book, there are many more titles available at **Stage 1** to build their reading skills:

The next step, **Read with Oxford Stage 2**, helps your child develop early reading skills. Here are just a few to get you started:

To see the whole **Read with Oxford** range and to learn more about the **Read with Oxford Stages**, have a look at **oxfordowl.co.uk**. You'll also find practical advice, free eBooks and fun activities to get your child off to a flying start!

Read with Oxford

Welcome to Read with Oxford

Featuring much-loved characters, great authors, engaging storylines and fun activities, **Read with Oxford** offers an exciting range of carefully levelled reading books to build your child's reading confidence.

From the very first steps in phonics all the way to reading independence, our unique and simple levelling system – **Read with Oxford Stages** – will guide you to choose the right book for your child.

For more information about **Read with Oxford Stages** and the whole range go to **oxfordowl.co.uk**. You'll also find lots of useful advice, free eBooks and activities to support your child through their learning journey.

Stories for wider reading

This story uses simple everyday language. Encourage your child to read as much as they can with you. You can help your child to read any longer words in the context of the story. Children enjoy re-reading stories and this helps to build their confidence and their vocabulary.

This book is part of the comprehensive and trusted range of support for learning at home from Oxford University Press.

You will find more advice and resources to support your child's learning on Oxford Owl.
www.oxfordowl.co.uk

Read with Oxford   **Progress with Oxford**   **Bond – exam preparation**   **Dictionaries**

Tips for reading *Dad's Birthday*

Children learn best when reading is relaxed and enjoyable.

- Talk about the title and look through the pictures so that your child can see what the story is about.
- Read the story to your child, placing your finger under each word as you read.
- Read the story again and encourage your child to join in.
- Give lots of praise as your child reads with you.
- Talk about the story.
- Do the fun activity on page 22.

Children enjoy re-reading stories and this helps to build their confidence.

Have fun!

After you have read the story, find the caterpillar hidden in every picture.

This book includes these useful common words:
go   had   on   Dad   said

For more activities, free eBooks and practical advice to help your child progress with reading visit **oxfordowl.co.uk**

Dad's Birthday

Written by Cynthia Rider,
based on the original characters
created by Roderick Hunt and Alex Brychta
Illustrated by Alex Brychta

OXFORD
UNIVERSITY PRESS

It was Dad's birthday.

Dad had a cake.

He had a bike.

Dad got on the bike.

"Go on, Dad," said Biff.

"Go on, Dad," said Chip.

"Go on, Dad," said Kipper.

Dad fell off!

Oh no!

Talk about the story

How did Dad make the children laugh when he was on the bike?

Why did Dad fall off the bike? Why isn't it a good idea to stand on a bike like that?

How do you think everyone felt when Floppy ran away with the cake?

Do you like going to parties? What is the best party you have been to?

Matching

Match the parcels to the presents.

OXFORD
UNIVERSITY PRESS

Great Clarendon Street, Oxford OX2 6DP

Oxford University Press is a department of the University of Oxford.
It furthers the University's objective of excellence in research, scholarship,
and education by publishing worldwide. Oxford is a registered trade mark
of Oxford University Press in the UK and in certain other countries

Text © Cynthia Rider 2005
Illustrations © Alex Brychta 2005

First published 2005. This edition published 2020.

Series Editors: Kate Ruttle, Annemarie Young

British Library Cataloguing in Publication Data available

ISBN: 978-0-19-277402-6

10 9 8 7 6 5 4 3 2

Printed in China

Paper used in the production of this book is a natural,
recyclable product made from wood grown in sustainable forests.
The manufacturing process conforms to the environmental
regulations of the country of origin.

Dad's Birthday is a **Read** with **Oxford Stage 1** book for children who are taking their first steps in reading. If your child enjoyed this book, there are many more titles available at **Stage 1** to build their reading skills:

The next step, **Read** with **Oxford Stage 2**, helps your child develop early reading skills. Here are just a few to get you started:

To see the whole **Read** with **Oxford** range and to learn more about the **Read** with **Oxford Stages**, have a look at **oxfordowl.co.uk**. You'll also find practical advice, free eBooks and fun activities to get your child off to a flying start!

Read with Oxford

Welcome to Read with Oxford

Featuring much-loved characters, great authors, engaging storylines and fun activities, **Read with Oxford** offers an exciting range of carefully levelled reading books to build your child's reading confidence.

From the very first steps in phonics all the way to reading independence, our unique and simple levelling system – **Read with Oxford Stages** – will guide you to choose the right book for your child.

For more information about **Read with Oxford Stages** and the whole range go to **oxfordowl.co.uk**. You'll also find lots of useful advice, free eBooks and activities to support your child through their learning journey.

Helping your child with phonics

Phonics is a way of teaching reading that is used in Primary schools. Children are taught to read letters or groups of letters by saying the sound(s) they represent; so they are taught the letter 'm' sounds like 'mmm' when we say it. Children are then taught more sounds, and learn to blend them to read words.

This book is part of the comprehensive and trusted range of support for learning at home from Oxford University Press.

You will find more advice and resources to support your child's learning on Oxford Owl.
www.oxfordowl.co.uk

Read with Oxford

Progress with Oxford

Bond – exam preparation

Dictionaries

Tips for reading *A Yak at the Picnic*

This book has two stories: *A Yak at the Picnic* (page 3) and *A Man in the Mud* (page 17).

- Talk about the title and the picture on the front cover and title pages of each story.

- Find the letters *y* and *u* in these titles and talk about the sounds they make when you read them in these words.

- Look at the *k*, *u*, *y*, *j* and *ck* words on pages 4 and 15. Say the sounds in each word and then say the word (e.g. *J-a-ck, Jack*).

- Read the stories and find the words with the letters *k*, *u*, *y*, *j* and *ck* in them.

- Do the fun activities at the end of each story.

Children enjoy re-reading stories and this helps to build their confidence.

Have fun!

After you have read *A Yak at the Picnic*, find seven squirrels in the pictures.

The main sounds practised in this book are 'k' as in *king*, 'u' as in *mud*, 'y' as in *yellow*, 'j' as in *jet*, 'ck' as in *back*.

For more activities, free eBooks and practical advice to help your child progress with reading visit **oxfordowl.co.uk**

A Yak at the Picnic

Written by Roderick Hunt
Illustrated by Nick Schon,
based on the original characters
created by Roderick Hunt and Alex Brychta

OXFORD

UNIVERSITY PRESS

Read these words

yum

neck

back

tubs

yak

Jack

cups

bull

Mum set up the picnic.

An odd animal ran up.

It was a yak.

Mum put lids back on the tubs.

The yak was lost.

A man ran up.

It was his lost yak.

The man got Jack the yak back.

Talk about the story

What did the yak eat?

Where had the yak come from?

What was the yak's name?

Which animals have you seen on a picnic?

13

Word search

What words can you find with *k, ck* or *y* in them?

Can you write them down?

a	k	i	m	t
s	o	c	k	s
o	d	e	c	k
y	u	m	f	d
r	p	a	c	k

Missing letters

Choose the letters to make a word

ck   y

_ak

Ja_

ba_

15

16

A man
in the mud

Written by Roderick Hunt
Illustrated by Nick Schon,
based on the original characters
created by Roderick Hunt and Alex Brychta

OXFORD
UNIVERSITY PRESS

Read these words

mud

moss

fun

will

deck

mess

zap

jet

Gran had mud on her deck.

Gran had moss on the deck.

It is a mess.

Gran had to get rid of it.

She got a jet.

The jet will zap it.

The jet was fun.

Gran did a dog.

Gran did a man.

Talk about the story

There was mud on Gran's deck. What else was there?

Why did Gran like using the jet?

What did Gran draw on the deck?

What would you have drawn on the deck?

Missing letters

Choose the letters to make a word:

u   ss   j

f_n

_et

me__

m_d

fu_

What's in the picture?

Match the words to things you can find in the picture.
Point to the ones you can find.

Dad mud dog mess cat Mum jet

Spot the difference

Find the five differences in the two pictures.

OXFORD
UNIVERSITY PRESS

Great Clarendon Street, Oxford OX2 6DP

Oxford University Press is a department of the University of Oxford.
It furthers the University's objective of excellence in research, scholarship,
and education by publishing worldwide. Oxford is a registered trade mark
of Oxford University Press in the UK and in certain other countries

Text © Roderick Hunt 2014
Illustrations © Oxford University Press 2014

First published 2014. This edition published 2020.

Series Editors: Kate Ruttle, Annemarie Young

British Library Cataloguing in Publication Data available

ISBN: 978-0-19-277401-9

10 9 8 7 6 5 4 3 2

Printed in China

Paper used in the production of this book is a natural,
recyclable product made from wood grown in sustainable forests.
The manufacturing process conforms to the environmental
regulations of the country of origin.

A Yak at the Picnic is a **Read** with **Oxford Stage 1** book for children who are taking their first steps in reading. If your child enjoyed this book, there are many more titles available at **Stage 1** to build their reading skills:

The next step, **Read** with **Oxford Stage 2**, helps your child develop early reading skills. Here are just a few to get you started:

To see the whole **Read** with **Oxford** range and to learn more about the **Read** with **Oxford Stages**, have a look at **oxfordowl.co.uk**. You'll also find practical advice, free eBooks and fun activities to get your child off to a flying start!

Read with Oxford

Welcome to Read with Oxford

Featuring much-loved characters, great authors, engaging storylines and fun activities, **Read with Oxford** offers an exciting range of carefully levelled reading books to build your child's reading confidence.

From the very first steps in phonics all the way to reading independence, our unique and simple levelling system – **Read with Oxford Stages** – will guide you to choose the right book for your child.

For more information about **Read with Oxford Stages** and the whole range go to **oxfordowl.co.uk**. You'll also find lots of useful advice, free eBooks and activities to support your child through their learning journey.

Helping your child with phonics

Phonics is a way of teaching reading that is used in Primary schools. Children are taught to read letters or groups of letters by saying the sound(s) they represent; so they are taught the letter 'm' sounds like 'mmm' when we say it. Children are then taught more sounds, and learn to blend them to read words.

This book is part of the comprehensive and trusted range of support for learning at home from Oxford University Press.

You will find more advice and resources to support your child's learning on Oxford Owl. **www.oxfordowl.co.uk**

Read with Oxford   **Progress with Oxford**   **Bond – exam preparation**   **Dictionaries**

Tips for reading *The Fizz-Buzz*

This book contains two stories: *The Fizz-Buzz* (page 3) and *Less Mess* (page 17).

- Talk about the title and the picture on the front cover and the title pages of each story.
- Find the letters *zz* and *ss* in these titles and talk about the sounds they make when you read them in these words.
- Look at the *zz, z, ss, ff, f* and *j* words on pages 4 and 16. Say the sounds in each word and then say the word (e.g. *B-u-zz, Buzz*).
- Read the stories and find the words with the letters *zz, z, ss, ff,* and *j* in them.
- Do the fun activities at the end of each story.

Children enjoy re-reading stories and this helps to build their confidence.

Have fun!

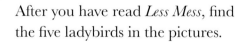
After you have read *Less Mess*, find the five ladybirds in the pictures.

The main sounds practised in this book are 'z' as in *zap* and *buzz*, 's' as in *mess*, 'f' as in *off* and *fizz*, and 'j' as in *jam*.

For more activities, free eBooks and practical advice to help your child progress with reading visit **oxfordowl.co.uk**

The Fizz–Buzz

Written by Roderick Hunt
Illustrated by Alex Brychta

OXFORD
UNIVERSITY PRESS

Read these words

zip

fizz

buzz

off

zap

puff

Dad had a Zip-zap.

Let it off, Dad.

Off it went.

Zip!

Zap!

Dad had a Fizz-buzz.

But it did not go off.

The Fizz-buzz went puff.

puff

The Fizz-buzz went off!

Up it went.

Dad fell in the mud.

He got wet.

Fizz!
Buzz!

"Buzz off," said Dad.

Talk about the story

What fireworks did Dad have?

Which one went 'puff'?

Why did Dad fall in the mud?

What fireworks have you seen?

15

Spot the difference

Find the five differences in the two pictures.

Less mess

Written by Roderick Hunt
Illustrated by Alex Brychta

OXFORD
UNIVERSITY PRESS

Read these words

fuss	less
mess	jam
jug	mix

"Put it all in," said Dad.
"Fill up the jug."

"Put in lots of jam," said Dad.

21

"Mix it all up," said Dad.

23

Dad did not put the lid on.

"Mop it up," said Mum. "No fuss."

26

"We got rid of the mess,"
said Dad.

Talk about the story

What did Dad put in the jug?

What did Biff tell Dad?

What made the mess?

What do you like to make in the kitchen?

Maze

Help the firework get up into the sky.

OXFORD
UNIVERSITY PRESS

Great Clarendon Street, Oxford OX2 6DP

Oxford University Press is a department of the University of Oxford.
It furthers the University's objective of excellence in research, scholarship,
and education by publishing worldwide. Oxford is a registered trade mark
of Oxford University Press in the UK and in certain other countries

First published 2007. This edition published 2020.

Series Editors: Kate Ruttle, Annemarie Young

British Library Cataloguing in Publication Data available

ISBN: 978-0-19-277393-7

10 9 8 7 6 5 4 3 2

Printed in China

Paper used in the production of this book is a natural,
recyclable product made from wood grown in sustainable forests.
The manufacturing process conforms to the environmental
regulations of the country of origin.

The Fizz-Buzz is a **Read with Oxford Stage 1** book for children who are taking their first steps in reading. If your child enjoyed this book, there are many more titles available at **Stage 1** to build their reading skills:

The next step, **Read with Oxford Stage 2**, helps your child develop early reading skills. Here are just a few to get you started:

To see the whole **Read with Oxford** range and to learn more about the **Read with Oxford Stages**, have a look at **oxfordowl.co.uk**. You'll also find practical advice, free eBooks and fun activities to get your child off to a flying start!

Read with Oxford

Welcome to Read with Oxford

Featuring much-loved characters, great authors, engaging storylines and fun activities, **Read with Oxford** offers an exciting range of carefully levelled reading books to build your child's reading confidence.

From the very first steps in phonics all the way to reading independence, our unique and simple levelling system – **Read with Oxford Stages** – will guide you to choose the right book for your child.

For more information about **Read with Oxford Stages** and the whole range go to **oxfordowl.co.uk**. You'll also find lots of useful advice, free eBooks and activities to support your child through their learning journey.

Stories for wider reading

This story uses simple everyday language. Encourage your child to read as much as they can with you. You can help your child to read any longer words in the context of the story. Children enjoy re-reading stories and this helps to build their confidence and their vocabulary.

This book is part of the comprehensive and trusted range of support for learning at home from Oxford University Press.

You will find more advice and resources to support your child's learning on Oxford Owl. **www.oxfordowl.co.uk**

Read with Oxford   **Progress with Oxford**   **Bond – exam preparation**   **Dictionaries**

Tips for reading *The Snowman*

Children learn best when reading is relaxed and enjoyable.

- Talk about the title and the picture on the front cover.

- Look through the pictures together so your child can see what the story is about.

- Read the story to your child, placing your finger under each word as you read.

- Read the story again and encourage your child to join in.

- Talk about the story.

- Do the fun activity on page 22.

Children enjoy re-reading stories and this helps to build their confidence.

Have fun!

After you have read the story, find the robin hidden in every picture.

This book includes these useful common words:

had   it   no

For more activities, free eBooks and practical advice to help your child progress with reading visit **oxfordowl.co.uk**

The Snowman

Written by Cynthia Rider,
based on the original characters
created by Roderick Hunt and Alex Brychta
Illustrated by Alex Brychta

OXFORD
UNIVERSITY PRESS

Biff   Chip   Wilma

Wilf   Kipper   Floppy

Wilma made a snowman.

It had a red nose.

It had a blue scarf.

It had green gloves.

It had a black hat.

The hat fell on Floppy.

Floppy ran.

Oh no!

No snowman!

Talk about the story

What are the colours the snowman is wearing?

Why did Floppy run off?

What else could you put on the snowman?

What would you like to make with snow or sand?

21

Fun activity

Find the twin snowmen.

OXFORD
UNIVERSITY PRESS

Great Clarendon Street, Oxford OX2 6DP

Oxford University Press is a department of the University of Oxford.
It furthers the University's objective of excellence in research, scholarship,
and education by publishing worldwide. Oxford is a registered trade mark
of Oxford University Press in the UK and in certain other countries

Text © Cynthia Rider 2005
Illustrations © Alex Brychta 2005

First published 2005. This edition published 2020.

Series Editors: Kate Ruttle, Annemarie Young

British Library Cataloguing in Publication Data available

ISBN: 978-0-19-277410-1

10 9 8 7 6 5 4 3 2

Printed in China

Paper used in the production of this book is a natural,
recyclable product made from wood grown in sustainable forests.
The manufacturing process conforms to the environmental
regulations of the country of origin.

The Snowman is a **Read with Oxford Stage 1** book for children who are taking their first steps in reading. If your child enjoyed this book, there are many more titles available at **Stage 1** to build their reading skills:

The next step, **Read with Oxford Stage 2**, helps your child develop early reading skills. Here are just a few to get you started:

To see the whole **Read with Oxford** range and to learn more about the **Read with Oxford Stages**, have a look at **oxfordowl.co.uk**. You'll also find practical advice, free eBooks and fun activities to get your child off to a flying start!

Read with Oxford

Welcome to Read with Oxford

Featuring much-loved characters, great authors, engaging storylines and fun activities, **Read with Oxford** offers an exciting range of carefully levelled reading books to build your child's reading confidence.

From the very first steps in phonics all the way to reading independence, our unique and simple levelling system – **Read with Oxford Stages** – will guide you to choose the right book for your child.

For more information about **Read with Oxford Stages** and the whole range go to **oxfordowl.co.uk**. You'll also find lots of useful advice, free eBooks and activities to support your child through their learning journey.

Stories for wider reading

This story uses simple everyday language. Encourage your child to read as much as they can with you. You can help your child to read any longer words in the context of the story. Children enjoy re-reading stories and this helps to build their confidence and their vocabulary.

This book is part of the comprehensive and trusted range of support for learning at home from Oxford University Press.

You will find more advice and resources to support your child's learning on Oxford Owl. **oxfordowl.co.uk**.

Read with Oxford

Progress with Oxford

Bond – exam preparation

Dictionaries

Tips for reading *Silly Races*

Children learn best when reading is relaxed and enjoyable.

- Talk about the title and look through the pictures so that your child can see what the story is about.
- Read the story to your child, placing your finger under each word as you read.
- Read the story again and encourage your child to join in.
- Give lots of praise as your child reads with you.
- Talk about the story.
- Do the fun activity on page 22.

Children enjoy re-reading stories and this helps to build their confidence.

Have fun!

After you have read the story, find the bird hidden in every picture.

This book includes these useful common words:

an   got   ran   Dad

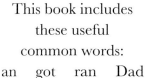

For more activities, free eBooks and practical advice to help your child progress with reading visit **oxfordowl.co.uk**

Silly Races

Written by Roderick Hunt
Illustrated by Alex Brychta

OXFORD
UNIVERSITY PRESS

Kipper ran.

Kipper got a banana.

Mum ran.

She got an apple.

Biff and Chip ran.

Finish

They got an orange.

Dad ran.

Floppy ran.

18

Oh no! Dad fell.

Dad got a duck!

Talk about the story

Why are they silly races?

Which race do you think is the funniest?

Which of the races would you like to be in?

What other sorts of races do people do?

21

Spot the difference

Find the five differences in the two paddling pools.

OXFORD
UNIVERSITY PRESS

Great Clarendon Street, Oxford OX2 6DP

Oxford University Press is a department of the University of Oxford.
It furthers the University's objective of excellence in research, scholarship,
and education by publishing worldwide. Oxford is a registered trade mark
of Oxford University Press in the UK and in certain other countries

Text © Roderick Hunt 2005
Illustrations © Alex Brychta 2005

First published 2005. This edition published 2020.

Series Editors: Kate Ruttle, Annemarie Young

British Library Cataloguing in Publication Data available

ISBN: 978-0-19-277408-8

10 9 8 7 6 5 4 3 2

Printed in China

Paper used in the production of this book is a natural,
recyclable product made from wood grown in sustainable forests.
The manufacturing process conforms to the environmental
regulations of the country of origin.

Silly Races is a **Read** with **Oxford Stage 1** book for children who are taking their first steps in reading. If your child enjoyed this book, there are many more titles available at **Stage 1** to build their reading skills:

The next step, **Read** with **Oxford Stage 2**, helps your child develop early reading skills. Here are just a few to get you started:

To see the whole **Read** with **Oxford** range and to learn more about the **Read** with **Oxford Stages**, have a look at **oxfordowl.co.uk**. You'll also find practical advice, free eBooks and fun activities to get your child off to a flying start!

Read with Oxford

Welcome to Read with Oxford

Featuring much-loved characters, great authors, engaging storylines and fun activities, **Read with Oxford** offers an exciting range of carefully levelled reading books to build your child's reading confidence.

From the very first steps in phonics all the way to reading independence, our unique and simple levelling system – **Read with Oxford Stages** – will guide you to choose the right book for your child.

For more information about **Read with Oxford Stages** and the whole range go to **oxfordowl.co.uk**. You'll also find lots of useful advice, free eBooks and activities to support your child through their learning journey.

Stories for wider reading

This story uses simple everyday language. Encourage your child to read as much as they can with you. You can help your child to read any longer words in the context of the story. Children enjoy re-reading stories and this helps to build their confidence and their vocabulary.

This book is part of the comprehensive and trusted range of support for learning at home from Oxford University Press.

You will find more advice and resources to support your child's learning on Oxford Owl. **www.oxfordowl.co.uk**

Read with Oxford   **Progress with Oxford**   **Bond – exam preparation**   **Dictionaries**

Tips for reading *Funny Fish*

Children learn best when reading is relaxed and enjoyable.

- Talk about the title and the picture on the front cover.
- Look through the pictures together so your child can see what the story is about.
- Read the story to your child, placing your finger under each word as you read.
- Read the story again and encourage your child to join in.
- Talk about the story.
- Do the fun activity on page 22.

Children enjoy re-reading stories and this helps to build their confidence.

Have fun!

After you have read the story, find the starfish hidden in every picture.

This book includes these useful common words:
got   he   she   was

For more activities, free eBooks and practical advice to help your child progress with reading visit **oxfordowl.co.uk**

Funny Fish

Written by Cynthia Rider,
based on the original characters
created by Roderick Hunt and Alex Brychta
Illustrated by Alex Brychta

OXFORD

UNIVERSITY PRESS

Mum   Dad   Biff

Chip   Kipper   Floppy

Kipper was fishing.

He got a hat.

Biff was fishing.

She got a crab.

Chip was fishing.

He got an octopus!

Mum was fishing.

She got a bucket.

14

Dad was fishing.

He got a boot.

SPLASH!

Floppy got a fish!

Talk about the story

Why do you think Floppy fell into the water?

Who do you think caught the funniest fish?

What would you do if you caught a big crab, like Biff?

Floppy's fish lives in the sea. Where else do fish live?

Tangled lines

Follow the lines to see who gets the fish.

OXFORD
UNIVERSITY PRESS

Great Clarendon Street, Oxford OX2 6DP

Oxford University Press is a department of the University of Oxford.
It furthers the University's objective of excellence in research, scholarship,
and education by publishing worldwide. Oxford is a registered trade mark
of Oxford University Press in the UK and in certain other countries

Text © Cynthia Rider 2005
Illustrations © Alex Brychta 2005

First published 2005. This edition published 2020.

Series Editors: Kate Ruttle, Annemarie Young

British Library Cataloguing in Publication Data available

ISBN: 978-0-19-277404-0

10 9 8 7 6 5 4 3 2

Printed in China

Paper used in the production of this book is a natural,
recyclable product made from wood grown in sustainable forests.
The manufacturing process conforms to the environmental
regulations of the country of origin.

Funny Fish is a **Read** with **Oxford Stage 1** book for children who are taking their first steps in reading. If your child enjoyed this book, there are many more titles available at **Stage 1** to build their reading skills:

The next step, **Read** with **Oxford Stage 2**, helps your child develop early reading skills. Here are just a few to get you started:

To see the whole **Read** with **Oxford** range and to learn more about the **Read** with **Oxford Stages**, have a look at **oxfordowl.co.uk**. You'll also find practical advice, free eBooks and fun activities to get your child off to a flying start!

Read with Oxford

Welcome to Read with Oxford

Featuring much-loved characters, great authors, engaging storylines and fun activities, **Read with Oxford** offers an exciting range of carefully levelled reading books to build your child's reading confidence.

From the very first steps in phonics all the way to reading independence, our unique and simple levelling system – **Read with Oxford Stages** – will guide you to choose the right book for your child.

For more information about **Read with Oxford Stages** and the whole range go to **oxfordowl.co.uk**. You'll also find lots of useful advice, free eBooks and activities to support your child through their learning journey.

Helping your child with phonics

Phonics is a way of teaching reading that is used in Primary schools. Children are taught to read letters or groups of letters by saying the sound(s) they represent; so they are taught the letter 'm' sounds like 'mmm' when we say it. Children are then taught more sounds, and learn to blend them to read words.

This book is part of the comprehensive and trusted range of support for learning at home from Oxford University Press.

You will find more advice and resources to support your child's learning on Oxford Owl. **www.oxfordowl.co.uk**

Read with Oxford **Progress with Oxford** **Bond – exam preparation** **Dictionaries**

Tips for reading *The Red Hen*

This book contains two stories: *The Red Hen* (page 3) and *Tip Top* (page 17).

- Talk about the title and the picture on the front cover and the title pages of each story.

- Find the letters *e* and *i* in these titles and talk about the sounds they make when you read them in these words.

- Look at the *e*, *o*, *a*, *i* and *ss* words on pages 4 and 15. Say the sounds in each word and then say the word (e.g. *T-e-ss*, *Tess*).

- Read the stories and find the words with the letters *e*, *o*, *a*, *i* and *ss* in them.

- Do the fun activities at the end of each story.

Children enjoy re-reading stories and this helps to build their confidence.

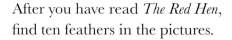

Have fun!

After you have read *The Red Hen*, find ten feathers in the pictures.

The main sounds practised in this book are 'e' as in *hen*, 'o' as in *pot*, 'a' as in *bag*, 's' as in *Tess*, and 'i' as in *tin*.

For more activities, free eBooks and practical advice to help your child progress with reading visit **oxfordowl.co.uk**

The Red Hen

Written by Roderick Hunt
Illustrated by Nick Schon,
based on the original characters
created by Roderick Hunt and Alex Brychta

OXFORD

UNIVERSITY PRESS

Read these words

hen   pen

net   Tess

not   got

box   pot

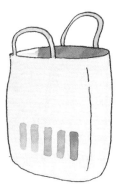

Tess the hen was not in the pen.

Dad had a net.

Mum had a bag.

I can get Tess!

Tess ran.

Mum ran and Dad ran.

Chip did not run.

9

Chip got a big box.

He set the box up.

He put in a pot.

Chip got Tess in the box.

Dad put Tess in the pen.

Talk about the story

What did Mum use to try to catch Tess?

What did Chip do to catch Tess?

Why did Tess go under the box?

How do you help out at home?

13

Missing letters

Put in the missing letter to make the word.

e a o

h__n   p__n

b__g   n__t

g__t   p__t

14

Spot the difference

Find the five differences in the two pictures.

Tip Top

Written by Roderick Hunt
Illustrated by Nick Schon,
based on the original characters
created by Roderick Hunt and Alex Brychta

OXFORD
UNIVERSITY PRESS

Read these words

big	tin
bin	tip
wok	top
box	on

Kipper had a big box.

He put a wok on top.

Kipper put a bin on the wok.

He put a tin on the bin.

Kipper set a jug on the tin.

He put a pan on the jug.

Kipper put a mug on the pan,

It will tip!

and he set Ted on top.

It did tip!

Talk about the story

What did Kipper put on the tin?

What did Kipper put on the pan?

Why did the tower tip?

What have you used to build towers? Did your tower tip?

27

What's in the picture?

What are the things in the picture that have *e* and *u* in the middle of the word? Find something in the picture that has *a* in the middle of the word. Find the three things that have *u* in the middle of the word.

pan; mug, jug, mum

Spot the difference

Find the five differences in the two pictures.

Maze

Help Chip get to Tess.

OXFORD
UNIVERSITY PRESS

Great Clarendon Street, Oxford OX2 6DP

Oxford University Press is a department of the University of Oxford.
It furthers the University's objective of excellence in research, scholarship,
and education by publishing worldwide. Oxford is a registered trade mark
of Oxford University Press in the UK and in certain other countries

Text © Roderick Hunt 2007
Illustrations © Alex Brychta and Nick Schon 2007

First published 2007. This edition published 2020.

Series Editors: Kate Ruttle, Annemarie Young

British Library Cataloguing in Publication Data available

ISBN: 978-0-19-277399-9

10 9 8 7 6 5 4 3 2

Printed in China

Paper used in the production of this book is a natural,
recyclable product made from wood grown in sustainable forests.
The manufacturing process conforms to the environmental
regulations of the country of origin.

The Red Hen is a **Read with Oxford Stage 1** book for children who are taking their first steps in reading. If your child enjoyed this book, there are many more titles available at **Stage 1** to build their reading skills:

The next step, **Read with Oxford Stage 2**, helps your child develop early reading skills. Here are just a few to get you started:

To see the whole **Read with Oxford** range and to learn more about the **Read with Oxford Stages**, have a look at **oxfordowl.co.uk**. You'll also find practical advice, free eBooks and fun activities to get your child off to a flying start!

Welcome to Read with Oxford

Featuring much-loved characters, great authors, engaging storylines and fun activities, **Read with Oxford** offers an exciting range of carefully levelled reading books to build your child's reading confidence.

From the very first steps in phonics all the way to reading independence, our unique and simple levelling system – **Read with Oxford Stages** – will guide you to choose the right book for your child.

For more information about **Read with Oxford Stages** and the whole range go to **oxfordowl.co.uk**. You'll also find lots of useful advice, free eBooks and activities to support your child through their learning journey.

Helping your child with phonics

Phonics is a way of teaching reading that is used in Primary schools. Children are taught to read letters or groups of letters by saying the sound(s) they represent; so they are taught the letter 'm' sounds like 'mmm' when we say it. Children are then taught more sounds, and learn to blend them to read words.

This book is part of the comprehensive and trusted range of support for learning at home from Oxford University Press.

You will find more advice and resources to support your child's learning on Oxford Owl. **www.oxfordowl.co.uk**

Read with Oxford   **Progress with Oxford**   **Bond – exam preparation**   **Dictionaries**

Tips for reading *Biff's Fun Phonics*

Children learn best when reading is relaxed and enjoyable.

- Tell your child that they are going to help Biff read and look for things in the pictures.

- Ask your child to read the captions and sentences on the left hand page. Then ask them to match them to the correct picture on the right hand page.

- Don't forget that when you talk about letter sounds, say the letter clearly, for example, for the sound 'm', you say 'mmm' not 'em'. You can listen to the letter sounds at **oxfordowl.co.uk**.

- Give lots of praise as your child reads with you and does the activities.

- Play the game on page 22 to help the muddy pup get to the bath.

Have fun!

After you have read the story, find the spider in every picture.

This book practises these letter sounds:
s a t p i n m d g o c c k
e u r h b f l v ff ll ss

For more activities, free eBooks and practical advice to help your child progress with reading visit **oxfordowl.co.uk**

Biff's Fun Phonics

Written by Annemarie Young,
based on the original characters
created by Roderick Hunt and Alex Brychta
Illustrated by Nick Schon

OXFORD
UNIVERSITY PRESS

Read the two captions.
Can you match each caption
to its picture?

a cap on a peg

a cup and a mug

Read the two captions.
Can you match each caption
to its picture?

cod in a pan

carrots in a pot

 Read the sentences. Which one matches the picture?

Hit the bell.

Fill the pot.

9

Read the captions. Can you find the rat and the hat in the picture?

a rat as big as a cat

a red hat in a red bag

Read these captions. Can you match the captions to the pictures?

red on the rug

mess on the mat

13

Read the sentences. Can you find the rabbit and the pup in the picture?

The rabbit is in the hut.

The pup is in the mud.

15

Read the sentences. Which
one matches the picture?

Get off the bus.

Get a hug and a kiss.

dy Fashions

 Read the sentences. Which one
matches the picture?

A nut on the bag.

Get on top of the rock.

19

Read the sentences. Can you
find the rabbit and the duck in
the picture?

The rabbit is at the vet.

The duck is on top.

21

Muddy maze

Help the muddy pup get to the bath.

OXFORD
UNIVERSITY PRESS

Great Clarendon Street, Oxford OX2 6DP

Oxford University Press is a department of the University of Oxford.
It furthers the University's objective of excellence in research, scholarship,
and education by publishing worldwide. Oxford is a registered trade mark
of Oxford University Press in the UK and in certain other countries

Text © Oxford University Press 2014
Illustrations © Oxford University Press 2014

First published 2014. This edition published 2020.

Series Editors: Kate Ruttle, Annemarie Young

British Library Cataloguing in Publication Data available

ISBN: 978-0-19-277389-0

10 9 8 7 6 5 4 3 2

Printed in China

Paper used in the production of this book is a natural,
recyclable product made from wood grown in sustainable forests.
The manufacturing process conforms to the environmental
regulations of the country of origin.

Biff's Fun Phonics is a **Read** with **Oxford Stage 1** book for children who are taking their first steps in reading. If your child enjoyed this book, there are many more titles available at **Stage 1** to build their reading skills:

The next step, **Read** with **Oxford Stage 2**, helps your child develop early reading skills. Here are just a few to get you started:

To see the whole **Read** with **Oxford** range and to learn more about the **Read** with **Oxford Stages**, have a look at **oxfordowl.co.uk**. You'll also find practical advice, free eBooks and fun activities to get your child off to a flying start!

Welcome to Read with Oxford

Featuring much-loved characters, great authors, engaging storylines and fun activities, **Read with Oxford** offers an exciting range of carefully levelled reading books to build your child's reading confidence.

From the very first steps in phonics all the way to reading independence, our unique and simple levelling system – **Read with Oxford Stages** – will guide you to choose the right book for your child.

For more information about **Read with Oxford Stages** and the whole range go to **oxfordowl.co.uk**. You'll also find lots of useful advice, free eBooks and activities to support your child through their learning journey.

Helping your child with phonics

Phonics is a way of teaching reading that is used in Primary schools. Children are taught to read letters or groups of letters by saying the sound(s) they represent; so they are taught the letter 'm' sounds like 'mmm' when we say it. Children are then taught more sounds, and learn to blend them to read words.

This book is part of the comprehensive and trusted range of support for learning at home from Oxford University Press.

You will find more advice and resources to support your child's learning on Oxford Owl. **www.oxfordowl.co.uk**

Read with Oxford   **Progress with Oxford**   **Bond – exam preparation**   **Dictionaries**

Tips for reading *Win a Nut*

This book has two stories: *Win a Nut* (page 3) and *The Bag on the Bus* (page 17).

- Talk about the title and the picture on the front cover and title pages of each story.

- Find the letters *u* and *i* in these titles and talk about the sounds they make when you read them in these words.

- Look at the *u, i, r, s* and *ff* words on pages 4 and 18. Say the sounds in each word and then say the word (e.g. *n-u-t, nut; o-ff, off*).

- Read the stories and find the words with the letters *u, i, r, s* and *ff* in them.

- Do the fun activities at the end of each story.

Children enjoy re-reading stories and this helps to build their confidence.

Have fun!

After you have read *Win a Nut*, find seven snails in the pictures.

The main sounds practised in this book are 'u' as in *nut*, 'i' as in *win*, 'r' as in *ran*, 's' as in *bus*, 'ff' as in *off*.

For more activities, free eBooks and practical advice to help your child progress with reading visit **oxfordowl.co.uk**

Win a Nut

Written by Roderick Hunt
Illustrated by Nick Schon,
based on the original characters
created by Roderick Hunt and Alex Brychta

OXFORD
UNIVERSITY PRESS

Read these words

hit   nut

did   off

luck   fuss

Mum   win

Can Dad hit a nut?

Dad hit a nut.

It did not fall off.

Can Mum win a nut?

Mum hit a nut, but it did not fall off.

Chip had a go.

Chip hit a nut!

The nut fell off.

Talk about the story

Who tried to win a coconut first?

Did Mum hit a coconut?

Why did Chip ask 'Is it a fix?'

What games have you played at a fair?

13

Missing letters

Choose the letters to make a word:

Ch_p

n_t

h_t

o__

14

Who did what?

Match each person to the thing they did.

The Bag on the Bus

Written by Roderick Hunt
Illustrated by Nick Schon,
based on the original characters
created by Roderick Hunt and Alex Brychta

Read these words

bus	run
stop	fun
hop	got
bag	ran

Mum and Biff got off the bus.

Mum's bag was on the bus.

My laptop is in the bag!

Mum ran and Biff ran.

Stop the bus!

Dad and Kipper ran.

Chip and Floppy ran.

Mum's bag is on the bus.

Mum got to the bus stop.

Mum got her bag back . . .

Mum got her laptop back.

Talk about the story

Who got off the bus?

What was in Mum's bag?

Why did Mum say it was no fun?

What kinds of things have you lost?

Missing letters

Choose the letters to make a word:

u   s

bu_

r_n

_top

f_n

Word search

How many words can you find with *r, u, s* or *ff* in them?

Can you write them down?

b	u	s	u	s
p	r	a	n	v
o	f	f	t	n
a	p	u	f	f
b	r	u	n	t

Mum's maze

Help Mum get to her bag.

OXFORD
UNIVERSITY PRESS

Great Clarendon Street, Oxford OX2 6DP

Oxford University Press is a department of the University of Oxford.
It furthers the University's objective of excellence in research, scholarship,
and education by publishing worldwide. Oxford is a registered trade mark
of Oxford University Press in the UK and in certain other countries

Text © Roderick Hunt 2014
Illustrations © Oxford University Press 2014

First published 2014. This edition published 2020.

Series Editors: Kate Ruttle, Annemarie Young

British Library Cataloguing in Publication Data available

ISBN: 978-0-19-277400-2

10 9 8 7 6 5 4 3 2

Printed in China

Win a Nut is a **Read with Oxford Stage 1** book for children who are taking their first steps in reading. If your child enjoyed this book, there are many more titles available at **Stage 1** to build their reading skills:

The next step, **Read with Oxford Stage 2**, helps your child develop early reading skills. Here are just a few to get you started:

To see the whole **Read with Oxford** range and to learn more about the **Read with Oxford Stages**, have a look at **oxfordowl.co.uk**. You'll also find practical advice, free eBooks and fun activities to get your child off to a flying start!

Welcome to Read with Oxford

Featuring much-loved characters, great authors, engaging storylines and fun activities, **Read with Oxford** offers an exciting range of carefully levelled reading books to build your child's reading confidence.

From the very first steps in phonics all the way to reading independence, our unique and simple levelling system – **Read with Oxford Stages** – will guide you to choose the right book for your child.

For more information about **Read with Oxford Stages** and the whole range go to **oxfordowl.co.uk**. You'll also find lots of useful advice, free eBooks and activities to support your child through their learning journey.

Helping your child with phonics

Phonics is a way of teaching reading that is used in Primary schools. Children are taught to read letters or groups of letters by saying the sound(s) they represent; so they are taught the letter 'm' sounds like 'mmm' when we say it. Children are then taught more sounds, and learn to blend them to read words.

This book is part of the comprehensive and trusted range of support for learning at home from Oxford University Press.

You will find more advice and resources to support your child's learning on Oxford Owl. **www.oxfordowl.co.uk**

Read with Oxford   **Progress with Oxford**   **Bond – exam preparation**   **Dictionaries**

Tips for reading *Biff's Wonder Words*

Children learn best when reading is relaxed and enjoyable.

- Tell your child they are going to help Biff to read words and play 'I spy'.

- Ask your child to read each of the words on the left hand page. Then ask them to find them in the scene on the right hand page.

- Once they have done this, ask them to do the activity on the right hand page: find objects where the words start or end with a particular letter, or find words that rhyme.

- Don't forget that when you talk about letter sounds, say the letter clearly, for example, for the sound 'm', you say 'mmm' not 'em'. You can listen to the letter sounds at **oxfordowl.co.uk**.

- Give lots of praise as your child plays the game with you.

- Do the odd one out puzzle on each page and the spot the difference activity on page 22.

Have fun!

Find the odd one out on every left hand page.

This book practises these letter sounds:

s a t p i n m d g o c k ck
e u r h b f ff ll ss

For more activities, free eBooks and practical advice to help your child progress with reading visit **oxfordowl.co.uk**

Biff's Wonder Words

Written by Kate Ruttle and Annemarie Young,
based on original characters created by
Roderick Hunt and Alex Brychta
Illustrated by Alex Brychta

OXFORD

UNIVERSITY PRESS

Help me read these words.
Can you find them in the picture?

Mum
Dad

dog, duck, door, drum, duckling, dandelion

4

5

Read these words and find them in the picture.

dog
cat

log, frog, bog

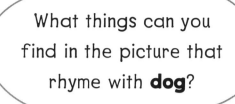

Read these words and find them in the picture.

mud

cap

web

water, wind, woodpecker

8

Did you find the web?
Find three other things in the
picture that start with **w**.

9

Read these words and find them in the picture.

bag

hat

pen

nut, mat, cat

10

11

Read these words and find them in the picture. Which words rhyme?

man
bus
cab
van

can, pan

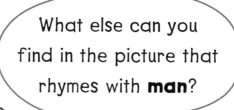

Read these words and find
them in the picture.

sun

cup

jam

log

14

Chip, cup, sheep

15

Read these words and find them in the picture. Which words rhyme?

hen
bug
leg
den

den, pen

16

What else is in the picture that rhymes with **hen**?

 Read these words and find
them in the picture.

mop

pot

mug

lid

tap

pot, dot, fruit, bucket, biscuit

18

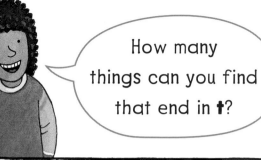

19

Read these words and
find them in the picture.

Biff

rug

bed

mess

sock

clock, mug, head

20

21

Spot the difference

Find the five differences in the two pictures of Biff.

UNIVERSITY PRESS

Great Clarendon Street, Oxford OX2 6DP

Oxford University Press is a department of the University of Oxford.
It furthers the University's objective of excellence in research, scholarship,
and education by publishing worldwide. Oxford is a registered trade mark
of Oxford University Press in the UK and in certain other countries

British Library Cataloguing in Publication Data available

ISBN: 978-0-19-277390-6

10 9 8 7 6 5 4 3 2

Printed in China

Biff's Wonder Words is a **Read with Oxford Stage 1** book for children who are taking their first steps in reading. If your child enjoyed this book, there are many more titles available at **Stage 1** to build their reading skills:

The next step, **Read with Oxford Stage 2**, helps your child develop early reading skills. Here are just a few to get you started:

To see the whole **Read with Oxford** range and to learn more about the **Read with Oxford Stages**, have a look at **oxfordowl.co.uk**. You'll also find practical advice, free eBooks and fun activities to get your child off to a flying start!

Welcome to Read with Oxford

Featuring much-loved characters, great authors, engaging storylines and fun activities, **Read with Oxford** offers an exciting range of carefully levelled reading books to build your child's reading confidence.

From the very first steps in phonics all the way to reading independence, our unique and simple levelling system – **Read with Oxford Stages** – will guide you to choose the right book for your child.

For more information about **Read with Oxford Stages** and the whole range go to **oxfordowl.co.uk**. You'll also find lots of useful advice, free eBooks and activities to support your child through their learning journey.

Stories for wider reading

These two stories use simple everyday language. Encourage your child to read as much as they can with you. You can help your child to read any longer words in the context of the story. Children enjoy re-reading stories and this helps to build their confidence and their vocabulary.

This book is part of the comprehensive and trusted range of support for learning at home from Oxford University Press.

You will find more advice and resources to support your child's learning on Oxford Owl.
www.oxfordowl.co.uk

Read with Oxford   **Progress with Oxford**   **Bond – exam preparation**   **Dictionaries**

Tips for reading *Get On*

This book has two stories: *Get On* (page 3) and *Who Can You See?* (page 13).

- For each story, look through the pictures so your child can see what the story is about.
- Read the story to your child, placing your finger under each word as you read.
- Read the story again and encourage your child to join in.
- Give lots of praise as your child reads with you.
- Talk about the story.
- Do the fun activities at the end of each story.

Children enjoy re-reading stories and this helps to build their confidence.

Have fun!

After you have read *Get On*, find a shell in every picture.

This book includes these useful common words:

get   on   got   and

For more activities, free eBooks and practical advice to help your child progress with reading visit **oxfordowl.co.uk**

Get On

Written by Roderick Hunt
Illustrated by Alex Brychta

Get on.

Get on, Biff.

Biff got on.

Get on, Chip.

Chip got on.

Get on, Kipper.

Kipper got on.

Oh, no!

Talk about the story

Maze

Help Biff and Chip get to the sea.

Who Can You See?

Written by Roderick Hunt
Illustrated by Alex Brychta

Who can you see?

Biff…

…and Chip.

Mum...

...and Kipper.

Floppy…

…and a spaceman.

No. It is Dad!

Talk about the story

Where was the family?

What shape did Chip make with his hands?

What was Dad wearing?

Which shapes can you make with your shadow?

Match the shadows

Can you match the shadows to the characters?

OXFORD

UNIVERSITY PRESS

Great Clarendon Street, Oxford OX2 6DP

Oxford University Press is a department of the University of Oxford.
It furthers the University's objective of excellence in research, scholarship,
and education by publishing worldwide. Oxford is a registered trade mark
of Oxford University Press in the UK and in certain other countries

Text © Roderick Hunt 2006
Illustrations © Alex Brychta 2006

First published 2006. This edition published 2020.

Series Editors: Kate Ruttle, Annemarie Young

British Library Cataloguing in Publication Data available

ISBN: 978-0-19-277405-7

10 9 8 7 6 5 4 3 2

Printed in China

Paper used in the production of this book is a natural,
recyclable product made from wood grown in sustainable forests.
The manufacturing process conforms to the environmental
regulations of the country of origin.

Get On is a **Read** with **Oxford Stage 1** book for children who are taking their first steps in reading. If your child enjoyed this book, there are many more titles available at **Stage 1** to build their reading skills:

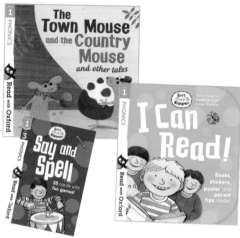

The next step, **Read** with **Oxford Stage 2**, helps your child develop early reading skills. Here are just a few to get you started:

To see the whole **Read** with **Oxford** range and to learn more about the **Read** with **Oxford Stages**, have a look at **oxfordowl.co.uk**. You'll also find practical advice, free eBooks and fun activities to get your child off to a flying start!

Read with **Oxford**

Welcome to Read with Oxford

Featuring much-loved characters, great authors, engaging storylines and fun activities, **Read with Oxford** offers an exciting range of carefully levelled reading books to build your child's reading confidence.

From the very first steps in phonics all the way to reading independence, our unique and simple levelling system – **Read with Oxford Stages** – will guide you to choose the right book for your child.

For more information about **Read with Oxford Stages** and the whole range go to **oxfordowl.co.uk**. You'll also find lots of useful advice, free eBooks and activities to support your child through their learning journey.

Stories for wider reading

These two stories use simple everyday language. Encourage your child to read as much as they can with you. You can help your child to read any longer words in the context of the story. Children enjoy re-reading stories and this helps to build their confidence and their vocabulary.

This book is part of the comprehensive and trusted range of support for learning at home from Oxford University Press.

You will find more advice and resources to support your child's learning on Oxford Owl. **www.oxfordowl.co.uk**

Read with Oxford   **Progress with Oxford**   **Bond – exam preparation**   **Dictionaries**

Tips for reading *Floppy Did This!*

This book has two stories: *Floppy Did This!* (page 3) and *Who Is It?* (page 13).

- For each story, look through the pictures, so your child can see what the story is about.
- Read the story to your child, placing your finger under each word as you read.
- Read the story again and encourage your child to join in.
- Give lots of praise as your child reads with you.
- Talk about the story.
- Do the fun activities at the end of each story.

Children enjoy re-reading stories and this helps to build their confidence.

Have fun!

After you have read *Floppy Did This!* find the paintbrush hidden in every picture.

This book includes these useful common words:

it   is   no

For more activities, free eBooks and practical advice to help your child progress with reading visit **oxfordowl.co.uk**

Floppy Did This!

Written by Roderick Hunt
Illustrated by Alex Brychta

Chip did this.

It is Biff.

Biff did this.

It is Kipper.

Kipper did this.

It is Mum.

Oh, no!

Floppy did this!

Talk about the story

Who drew a picture of Kipper?

Why are they all clapping Floppy?

Which picture do you like best?

Who have you drawn pictures of?

Spot the difference

Find the five differences in the two pictures of Kipper.

Who is it?

Written by Roderick Hunt
Illustrated by Alex Brychta

Who is it?

It is Kipper.

Who is it?

It is Biff.

Who is it?

It is Chip.

Is it Kipper?

No. It is Floppy!

Talk about the story

What was Kipper dressed up as on page 14?

What was Biff doing on page 15?

What was the trick on page 19?

What do you like dressing up as?

21

Twins

Find the twin clowns.

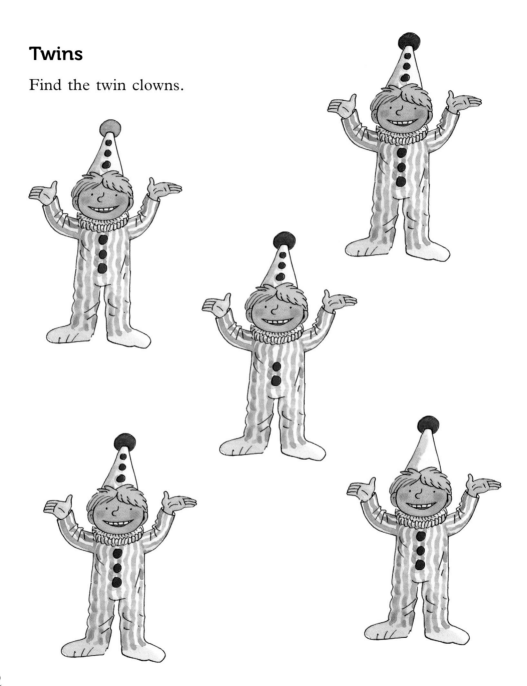

OXFORD
UNIVERSITY PRESS

Great Clarendon Street, Oxford OX2 6DP

Oxford University Press is a department of the University of Oxford.
It furthers the University's objective of excellence in research, scholarship,
and education by publishing worldwide. Oxford is a registered trade mark
of Oxford University Press in the UK and in certain other countries

First published 2006. This edition published 2020.

Series Editors: Kate Ruttle, Annemarie Young

British Library Cataloguing in Publication Data available

ISBN: 978-0-19-277403-3

10 9 8 7 6 5 4 3 2

Printed in China

Paper used in the production of this book is a natural,
recyclable product made from wood grown in sustainable forests.
The manufacturing process conforms to the environmental
regulations of the country of origin.

Floppy Did This! is a **Read with Oxford Stage 1** book for children who are taking their first steps in reading. If your child enjoyed this book, there are many more titles available at **Stage 1** to build their reading skills:

The next step, **Read with Oxford Stage 2**, helps your child develop early reading skills. Here are just a few to get you started:

To see the whole **Read with Oxford** range and to learn more about the **Read with Oxford Stages**, have a look at **oxfordowl.co.uk**. You'll also find practical advice, free eBooks and fun activities to get your child off to a flying start!

Read with Oxford

Welcome to Read with Oxford

Featuring much-loved characters, great authors, engaging storylines and fun activities, **Read with Oxford** offers an exciting range of carefully levelled reading books to build your child's reading confidence.

From the very first steps in phonics all the way to reading independence, our unique and simple levelling system – **Read with Oxford Stages** – will guide you to choose the right book for your child.

For more information about **Read with Oxford Stages** and the whole range go to **oxfordowl.co.uk**. You'll also find lots of useful advice, free eBooks and activities to support your child through their learning journey.

Stories for wider reading

These two stories use simple everyday language. Encourage your child to read as much as they can with you. You can help your child to read any longer words in the context of the story. Children enjoy re-reading stories and this helps to build their confidence and their vocabulary.

This book is part of the comprehensive and trusted range of support for learning at home from Oxford University Press.

You will find more advice and resources to support your child's learning on Oxford Owl. **www.oxfordowl.co.uk**

Read with Oxford   **Progress with Oxford**   **Bond – exam preparation**   **Dictionaries**

Tips for reading *A Good Trick*

This book has two stories: *A Good Trick* (page 3) and *Fun at the Beach* (page 13).

- For each story, look through the pictures so your child can see what the story is about.
- Read the story to your child, placing your finger under each word as you read.
- Read the story again and encourage your child to join in.
- Give lots of praise as your child reads with you.
- Talk about the story.
- Do the fun activities at the end of each story.

Children enjoy re-reading stories and this helps to build their confidence.

Have fun!

After you have read *Fun at the Beach*, find the butterfly in every picture.

This book includes these useful common words:

a   Dad   and   Mum

For more activities, free eBooks and practical advice to help your child progress with reading visit **oxfordowl.co.uk**

A Good Trick

Written by Roderick Hunt
Illustrated by Alex Brychta

A rug,

a sheet,

5

a big box,

a little box,

Kipper!

Talk about the story

Spot the difference

Find the five differences in the two pictures.

Fun at the Beach

Written by Roderick Hunt
Illustrated by Alex Brychta

Dad and Mum.

Mum and Dad.

Kipper, Chip and Biff.

Kipper, Biff and Dad.

Mum, Chip and Floppy.

Chip, Biff and Kipper.

18

Dad and Floppy.

19

Oh Floppy!

Talk about the story

Why do the children laugh at Mum and Dad?

Who plays on the trampolines?

How does Floppy get dirty?

What do you like to do at the beach?

Spot the pair

Find the identical pair.

OXFORD

UNIVERSITY PRESS

Great Clarendon Street, Oxford OX2 6DP

Oxford University Press is a department of the University of Oxford.
It furthers the University's objective of excellence in research, scholarship,
and education by publishing worldwide. Oxford is a registered trade mark
of Oxford University Press in the UK and in certain other countries

Text © Roderick Hunt 1998
Illustrations © Alex Brychta 1998

First published 1998. This edition published 2020.

Series Editors: Kate Ruttle, Annemarie Young

British Library Cataloguing in Publication Data available

ISBN: 978-0-19-277395-1

10 9 8 7 6 5 4 3 2

Printed in China

Paper used in the production of this book is a natural,
recyclable product made from wood grown in sustainable forests.
The manufacturing process conforms to the environmental
regulations of the country of origin.

A Good Trick is a **Read with Oxford Stage 1** book for children who are taking their first steps in reading. If your child enjoyed this book, there are many more titles available at **Stage 1** to build their reading skills:

The next step, **Read with Oxford Stage 2**, helps your child develop early reading skills. Here are just a few to get you started:

To see the whole **Read with Oxford** range and to learn more about the **Read with Oxford Stages**, have a look at **oxfordowl.co.uk**. You'll also find practical advice, free eBooks and fun activities to get your child off to a flying start!

Welcome to Read with Oxford

Featuring much-loved characters, great authors, engaging storylines and fun activities, **Read with Oxford** offers an exciting range of carefully levelled reading books to build your child's reading confidence.

From the very first steps in phonics all the way to reading independence, our unique and simple levelling system – **Read with Oxford Stages** – will guide you to choose the right book for your child.

For more information about **Read with Oxford Stages** and the whole range go to **oxfordowl.co.uk**. You'll also find lots of useful advice, free eBooks and activities to support your child through their learning journey.

Helping your child with phonics

Phonics is a way of teaching reading that is used in Primary schools. Children are taught to read letters or groups of letters by saying the sound(s) they represent; so they are taught the letter 'm' sounds like 'mmm' when we say it. Children are then taught more sounds, and learn to blend them to read words.

This book is part of the comprehensive and trusted range of support for learning at home from Oxford University Press.

You will find more advice and resources to support your child's learning on Oxford Owl.
www.oxfordowl.co.uk

Read with Oxford   **Progress with Oxford**   **Bond – exam preparation**   **Dictionaries**

Tips for reading *Kipper's Rhymes*

Children learn best when reading is relaxed and enjoyable.

- Tell your child that they are going to help Kipper read some fun rhymes and play 'I spy'.

- Ask your child to read the rhymes on the left hand page. Then ask them to find the objects in the scene on the right hand page.

- Once they have done this, ask them to find other rhyming objects in the picture.

- Don't forget that when you talk about letter sounds, say the letter clearly, for example, for the sound 'm', you say 'mmm' not 'em'. You can listen to the letter sounds at **oxfordowl.co.uk**.

- Give lots of praise as your child reads with you and does the activities.

- Play the game on page 22 to help Dad find his way home in the fog.

Have fun!

Find the robin hidden in every picture.

This book practises these letter sounds:
s a t p i n m d g o c k ck
e u r h b f l j w ff ll ss

For more activities, free eBooks and practical advice to help your child progress with reading visit **oxfordowl.co.uk**

Kipper's Rhymes

Written by Annemarie Young,
based on the original characters
created by Roderick Hunt and Alex Brychta
Illustrated by Alex Brychta

OXFORD
UNIVERSITY PRESS

Read these rhyming words and find them in the picture.

A bug in a mug.

A jug on the rug.

What else can you find in the picture that rhymes with **mug**?

hug, slug

Read these rhyming words and find
them in the picture.

A wet pet!

A fan and a can.

What other things
can you find in the
picture that rhyme with
pet and **can**?

jet, net, man, pan

Read these rhyming words and find
them in the picture.

Less mess, Biff!

Ted is on the bed.

What things can you
find in the picture that
rhyme with **sock**?

clock, rock

9

Read these rhyming words and find
them in the picture.

Hop to the top.

Bill is on the hill.

What else can you find in the picture that rhymes with **top**?

mop, pop

11

Read these rhyming words and find
them in the picture.

A dog on a log.

Huff and puff!

What else can you
find in the picture that
rhymes with **dog**?

fog, jog, bog

13

Read these rhyming words and find
them in the picture.

Jack and his backpack.

Mack in a sack.

What else can you
find in the picture that
rhymes with **sack**?

track

15

Read these rhyming words and find
them in the picture.

The hen is in a pen.

The egg is on
a peg.

What else can you
find in the picture that
rhymes with **pen**
and **peg**?

ten, men, leg

17

Read these rhyming words and find
them in the picture.

A ticket in a pocket.

A rocket in a bucket.

What else can you
find in the picture that
rhymes with **duck**?

truck

19

Read these rhyming words and find
them in the picture.

Pat a cat.

A rat sat on a mat.

What else can you
find in the picture that
rhymes with **cat**?

hat, bat

Maze haze

Help Dad get home in the fog.

OXFORD
UNIVERSITY PRESS

Great Clarendon Street, Oxford OX2 6DP

Oxford University Press is a department of the University of Oxford.
It furthers the University's objective of excellence in research, scholarship,
and education by publishing worldwide. Oxford is a registered trade mark
of Oxford University Press in the UK and in certain other countries

Text © Oxford University Press 2014
Illustrations © Alex Brychta 2014

First published 2014. This edition published 2020.

Series Editors: Kate Ruttle, Annemarie Young

British Library Cataloguing in Publication Data available

ISBN: 978-0-19-277398-2

10 9 8 7 6 5 4 3 2

Printed in China

Paper used in the production of this book is a natural,
recyclable product made from wood grown in sustainable forests.
The manufacturing process conforms to the environmental
regulations of the country of origin.

Kipper's Rhymes is a **Read with Oxford Stage 1** book for children who are taking their first steps in reading. If your child enjoyed this book, there are many more titles available at **Stage 1** to build their reading skills:

The next step, **Read with Oxford Stage 2**, helps your child develop early reading skills. Here are just a few to get you started:

To see the whole **Read with Oxford** range and to learn more about the **Read with Oxford Stages**, have a look at **oxfordowl.co.uk**. You'll also find practical advice, free eBooks and fun activities to get your child off to a flying start!

Welcome to Read with Oxford

Featuring much-loved characters, great authors, engaging storylines and fun activities, **Read with Oxford** offers an exciting range of carefully levelled reading books to build your child's reading confidence.

From the very first steps in phonics all the way to reading independence, our unique and simple levelling system – **Read with Oxford Stages** – will guide you to choose the right book for your child.

For more information about **Read with Oxford Stages** and the whole range go to **oxfordowl.co.uk**. You'll also find lots of useful advice, free eBooks and activities to support your child through their learning journey.

Stories for wider reading

These two stories use simple everyday language. Encourage your child to read as much as they can with you. You can help your child to read any longer words in the context of the story. Children enjoy re-reading stories and this helps to build their confidence and their vocabulary.

This book is part of the comprehensive and trusted range of support for learning at home from Oxford University Press.

You will find more advice and resources to support your child's learning on Oxford Owl. **www.oxfordowl.co.uk**

Read with Oxford   **Progress with Oxford**   **Bond – exam preparation**   **Dictionaries**

Tips for reading *Six in a Bed*

This book has two stories: *Six in a Bed* (page 3) and *Get Dad!* (page 13).

- For each story, look through the pictures so your child can see what the story is about.

- Read the story to your child, placing your finger under each word as you read.

- Read the story again and encourage your child to join in.

- Give lots of praise as your child reads with you.

- Talk about the story.

- Do the fun activities at the end of each story.

Children enjoy re-reading stories and this helps to build their confidence.

Have fun!

After you have read *Get Dad!*,
find the butterfly in every picture.

This book includes these
useful common words:
Mum   Dad   get   on   go

For more activities, free eBooks
and practical advice to help
your child progress with reading
visit **oxfordowl.co.uk**

Six in a Bed

Written by Roderick Hunt
Illustrated by Alex Brychta

Mum and Dad.

Mum, Kipper and Dad.

Mum, Kipper, Dad and Chip.

Biff, Mum, Kipper, Dad, Chip...

...and Floppy!

Talk about the story

Who got into bed with Mum and Dad first?

What did Kipper take with him?

Why did Floppy join in?

What do you like to do with all of your family?

Matching

Match the people with their belongings.

Get Dad!

Written by Roderick Hunt
Illustrated by Alex Brychta

Go on, Dad!

Get Biff.

Go on, Dad!

Get Chip.

Go on, Dad!

Get Kipper.

Go on, Mum!

Get Dad!

Talk about the story

What did Dad use to spray Biff?

How many different ways of making people wet can you remember?

Did Dad think he would get wet?

What do you like to play when it's hot?

Maze

Help the children get to Dad.

OXFORD
UNIVERSITY PRESS

Great Clarendon Street, Oxford OX2 6DP

Oxford University Press is a department of the University of Oxford.
It furthers the University's objective of excellence in research, scholarship,
and education by publishing worldwide. Oxford is a registered trade mark
of Oxford University Press in the UK and in certain other countries

Text © Roderick Hunt 2006
Illustrations © Alex Brychta 2006

First published 2006. This edition published 2020.

Series Editors: Kate Ruttle, Annemarie Young

British Library Cataloguing in Publication Data available

ISBN: 978-0-19-277409-5

10 9 8 7 6 5 4 3 2

Printed in China

Six in a Bed is a **Read** with **Oxford Stage 1** book for children who are taking their first steps in reading. If your child enjoyed this book, there are many more titles available at **Stage 1** to build their reading skills:

The next step, **Read** with **Oxford Stage 2**, helps your child develop early reading skills. Here are just a few to get you started:

To see the whole **Read** with **Oxford** range and to learn more about the **Read** with **Oxford Stages**, have a look at **oxfordowl.co.uk**. You'll also find practical advice, free eBooks and fun activities to get your child off to a flying start!

Read with **Oxford**

Welcome to Read with Oxford

Featuring much-loved characters, great authors, engaging storylines and fun activities, **Read with Oxford** offers an exciting range of carefully levelled reading books to build your child's reading confidence.

From the very first steps in phonics all the way to reading independence, our unique and simple levelling system – **Read with Oxford Stages** – will guide you to choose the right book for your child.

For more information about **Read with Oxford Stages** and the whole range go to **oxfordowl.co.uk**. You'll also find lots of useful advice, free eBooks and activities to support your child through their learning journey.

Stories for wider reading

These two stories use simple everyday language. Encourage your child to read as much as they can with you. You can help your child to read any longer words in the context of the story. Children enjoy re-reading stories and this helps to build their confidence and their vocabulary.

This book is part of the comprehensive and trusted range of support for learning at home from Oxford University Press.

You will find more advice and resources to support your child's learning on Oxford Owl. **www.oxfordowl.co.uk**

Read with Oxford   **Progress with Oxford**   **Bond – exam preparation**   **Dictionaries**

Tips for reading *The Pancake*

This book has two stories: *The Pancake* (page 3) and *Floppy Floppy* (page 13).

- For each story, look through the pictures so your child can see what the story is about.
- Read the story to your child, placing your finger under each word as you read.
- Read the story again and encourage your child to join in.
- Give lots of praise as your child reads with you.
- Talk about the story.
- Do the fun activities at the end of each story.

Children enjoy re-reading stories and this helps to build their confidence.

Have fun!

After you have read *Floppy Floppy*, find the caterpillar in every picture.

This book includes these common words:

the   no

For more activities, free eBooks and practical advice to help your child progress with reading visit **oxfordowl.co.uk**

The Pancake

Written by Roderick Hunt
Illustrated by Alex Brychta

The frying pan,

the flour,

the eggs,

the milk,

the butter,

the pancake.

The pancake race!

Talk about the story

Spot the difference

Find the five differences in the two pictures.

Floppy Floppy

Written by Roderick Hunt
Illustrated by Alex Brychta

Oh, Floppy!

No, Floppy!

Oh, Floppy!

17

No, Floppy!

Floppy Floppy.

Talk about the story

What does Floppy bury?

What does Floppy chase?

Why is Floppy tired?

What naughty pets do you know?

Match the shadows

Can you match the pictures of Floppy with
the shadows of Floppy?

OXFORD
UNIVERSITY PRESS

Great Clarendon Street, Oxford OX2 6DP

Oxford University Press is a department of the University of Oxford.
It furthers the University's objective of excellence in research, scholarship,
and education by publishing worldwide. Oxford is a registered trade mark
of Oxford University Press in the UK and in certain other countries

Text © Roderick Hunt 1998
Illustrations © Alex Brychta 1998

First published 1998. This edition published 2020.

Series Editors: Kate Ruttle, Annemarie Young

British Library Cataloguing in Publication Data available

ISBN: 978-0-19-277411-8

10 9 8 7 6 5 4 3 2

Printed in China

The Pancake is a **Read with Oxford Stage 1** book for children who are taking their first steps in reading. If your child enjoyed this book, there are many more titles available at **Stage 1** to build their reading skills:

The next step, **Read with Oxford Stage 2**, helps your child develop early reading skills. Here are just a few to get you started:

To see the whole **Read with Oxford** range and to learn more about the **Read with Oxford Stages**, have a look at **oxfordowl.co.uk**. You'll also find practical advice, free eBooks and fun activities to get your child off to a flying start!

Read with Oxford

Welcome to Read with Oxford

Featuring much-loved characters, great authors, engaging storylines and fun activities, **Read with Oxford** offers an exciting range of carefully levelled reading books to build your child's reading confidence.

From the very first steps in phonics all the way to reading independence, our unique and simple levelling system – **Read with Oxford Stages** – will guide you to choose the right book for your child.

For more information about **Read with Oxford Stages** and the whole range go to **oxfordowl.co.uk**. You'll also find lots of useful advice, free eBooks and activities to support your child through their learning journey.

Stories for wider reading

These two stories use simple everyday language. Encourage your child to read as much as they can with you. You can help your child to read any longer words in the context of the story. Children enjoy re-reading stories and this helps to build their confidence and their vocabulary.

This book is part of the comprehensive and trusted range of support for learning at home from Oxford University Press.

You will find more advice and resources to support your child's learning on Oxford Owl.
www.oxfordowl.co.uk

Read with Oxford

Progress with Oxford

Bond – exam preparation

Dictionaries

This book has two stories: *Up You Go* (page 3) and *I See* (page 13).

- For each story, look through the pictures so your child can see what the story is about.
- Read the story to your child, placing your finger under each word as you read.
- Read the story again and encourage your child to join in.
- Give lots of praise as your child reads with you.
- Talk about the story.
- Do the fun activities at the end of each story.

Children enjoy re-reading stories and this helps to build their confidence.

Have fun!

After you have read *Up You Go*, find the bee in every picture.

This book includes these useful common words:

go   no   I   Dad   up

For more activities, free eBooks and practical advice to help your child progress with reading visit **oxfordowl.co.uk**

Up You Go

Written by Roderick Hunt
Illustrated by Alex Brychta

Up you go, Kipper.

Go!

Up you go, Biff.

Go, go!

Chip, up you go.

Go, go, go!

No, Dad.

No, no, no!

Talk about the story

Who went down
the slide first?

What did Dad do
to the paddling
pool?

Why was Biff
laughing at Dad?

Which games
do you like to play
in the garden?

11

Spot the difference

Find the five differences in the two pictures of Kipper in the paddling pool.

I see

Written by Roderick Hunt
Illustrated by Alex Brychta

I see Biff.

I see Chip.

I see Mum and Dad.

We see Kipper.

We see Floppy.

I see Biff and Chip.

I see me!

Biff

Chip

Mum and Dad

Kipper

Floppy

Biff and Chip

20

Talk about the story

Where was Floppy?

How did Kipper look at Chip?

What was funny about Kipper's glasses?

What do you like to take photos of?

21

Matching

Help Kipper put the coloured shapes into the right holes.

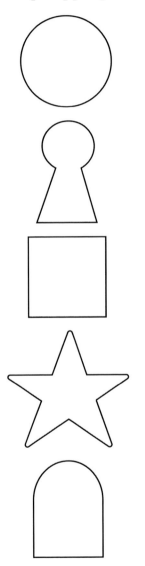
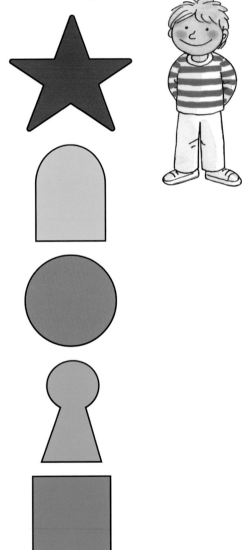

OXFORD
UNIVERSITY PRESS

Great Clarendon Street, Oxford OX2 6DP

Oxford University Press is a department of the University of Oxford.
It furthers the University's objective of excellence in research, scholarship,
and education by publishing worldwide. Oxford is a registered trade mark
of Oxford University Press in the UK and in certain other countries

Text © Roderick Hunt 2006
Illustrations © Alex Brychta 2006

First published 2006. This edition published 2020.

Series Editors: Kate Ruttle, Annemarie Young

British Library Cataloguing in Publication Data available

ISBN: 978-0-19-277412-5

10 9 8 7 6 5 4 3 2

Printed in China

The characters in this work are the original creation
of Roderick Hunt and Alex Brychta who retain copyright
in the characters.

Paper used in the production of this book is a natural,
recyclable product made from wood grown in sustainable forests.
The manufacturing process conforms to the environmental
regulations of the country of origin.

Up You Go is a **Read** with **Oxford Stage 1** book for children who are taking their first steps in reading. If your child enjoyed this book, there are many more titles available at **Stage 1** to build their reading skills:

The next step, **Read** with **Oxford Stage 2**, helps your child develop early reading skills. Here are just a few to get you started:

To see the whole **Read** with **Oxford** range and to learn more about the **Read** with **Oxford Stages**, have a look at **oxfordowl.co.uk**. You'll also find practical advice, free eBooks and fun activities to get your child off to a flying start!

Read with **Oxford**

Welcome to Read with Oxford

Featuring much-loved characters, great authors, engaging storylines and fun activities, **Read with Oxford** offers an exciting range of carefully levelled reading books to build your child's reading confidence.

From the very first steps in phonics all the way to reading independence, our unique and simple levelling system – **Read with Oxford Stages** – will guide you to choose the right book for your child.

For more information about **Read with Oxford Stages** and the whole range go to **oxfordowl.co.uk**. You'll also find lots of useful advice, free eBooks and activities to support your child through their learning journey.

Stories for wider reading

This story uses simple everyday language. Encourage your child to read as much as they can with you. You can help your child to read any longer words in the context of the story. Children enjoy re-reading stories and this helps to build their confidence and their vocabulary.

This book is part of the comprehensive and trusted range of support for learning at home from Oxford University Press.

You will find more advice and resources to support your child's learning on Oxford Owl.
www.oxfordowl.co.uk

Read with Oxford   **Progress with Oxford**   **Bond – exam preparation**   **Dictionaries**

Tips for reading *Picnic Time*

Children learn best when reading is relaxed and enjoyable.

- Talk about the title and the picture on the front cover.

- Look through the pictures so your child can see what the story is about.

- Read the story to your child, placing your finger under each word as you read.

- Read the story again and encourage your child to join in.

- Talk about the story.

- Do the fun activity on page 22.

Children enjoy re-reading stories and this helps to build their confidence.

Have fun!

After you have read the story, find the grasshopper hidden in every picture.

This book includes these useful common words:

said   on   some   came

For more activities, free eBooks and practical advice to help your child progress with reading visit **oxfordowl.co.uk**

Picnic Time

Written by Cynthia Rider,
based on the original characters
created by Roderick Hunt and Alex Brychta
Illustrated by Alex Brychta

OXFORD

UNIVERSITY PRESS

"Picnic time!" said Dad.

Biff sat on a log.

Some sheep came.

"Run!" said Kipper.

They sat on a bridge.

Some ducks came.

"Run!" said Chip.

They sat on a wall.

Some donkeys came.

"Run!" said Biff.

They sat on a rock.

Oh no! The rain came!

Talk about the story

What happened when Biff gave the duck some bread?

Why did the children run away from the animals?

Where was the picnic? How do you know?

What food would you like to take on a picnic?

21

Tangled lines

Who will get the picnic?

OXFORD
UNIVERSITY PRESS

Great Clarendon Street, Oxford OX2 6DP

Oxford University Press is a department of the University of Oxford.
It furthers the University's objective of excellence in research, scholarship,
and education by publishing worldwide. Oxford is a registered trade mark
of Oxford University Press in the UK and in certain other countries

Text © Cynthia Rider 2006
Illustrations © Alex Brychta 2006

First published 2006. This edition published 2020.

Series Editors: Kate Ruttle, Annemarie Young

British Library Cataloguing in Publication Data available

ISBN: 978-0-19-277407-1

10 9 8 7 6 5 4 3 2

Printed in China

Paper used in the production of this book is a natural,
recyclable product made from wood grown in sustainable forests.
The manufacturing process conforms to the environmental
regulations of the country of origin.

Picnic Time is a **Read** with **Oxford Stage 1** book for children who are taking their first steps in reading. If your child enjoyed this book, there are many more titles available at **Stage 1** to build their reading skills:

The next step, **Read** with **Oxford Stage 2**, helps your child develop early reading skills. Here are just a few to get you started:

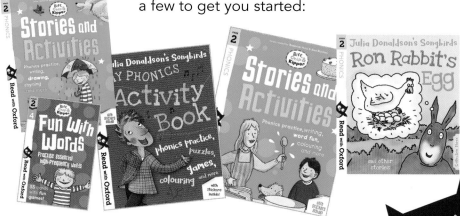

To see the whole **Read** with **Oxford** range and to learn more about the **Read** with **Oxford Stages**, have a look at **oxfordowl.co.uk**. You'll also find practical advice, free eBooks and fun activities to get your child off to a flying start!

Read with Oxford

Welcome to Read with Oxford

Featuring much-loved characters, great authors, engaging storylines and fun activities, **Read with Oxford** offers an exciting range of carefully levelled reading books to build your child's reading confidence.

From the very first steps in phonics all the way to reading independence, our unique and simple levelling system – **Read with Oxford Stages** – will guide you to choose the right book for your child.

For more information about **Read with Oxford Stages** and the whole range go to **oxfordowl.co.uk**. You'll also find lots of useful advice, free eBooks and activities to support your child through their learning journey.

Helping your child with phonics

Phonics is a way of teaching reading that is used in Primary schools. Children are taught to read letters or groups of letters by saying the sound(s) they represent; so they are taught the letter 'm' sounds like 'mmm' when we say it. Children are then taught more sounds, and learn to blend them to read words.

This book is part of the comprehensive and trusted range of support for learning at home from Oxford University Press.

You will find more advice and resources to support your child's learning on Oxford Owl.
www.oxfordowl.co.uk

Read with Oxford   **Progress with Oxford**   **Bond – exam preparation**   **Dictionaries**

Tips for reading *Chip's Letter Sounds*

Children learn best when reading is relaxed and enjoyable.

- Tell your child they are going to help Chip play 'I spy'.
- For each left-hand page, introduce the alphabet letter by saying its sound clearly, for example, make the sound of 's' as in sun. Don't say 'ess'.
- Ask them to trace the letters with their fingers while repeating the letter sound.
- Then ask your child to 'spy' things on the opposite page which begin with that letter sound. Look for lots of words!
- From page 10 enough letters have been introduced to make whole words. Read the 'word trail' with your child. Sound out each word then say the word (e.g. *h-o-p, hop*).
- Do the odd one out puzzle on each page and the tangled lines activity on page 22.

Have fun!

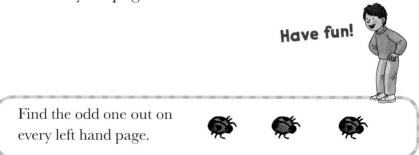

Find the odd one out on every left hand page.

This book practises these letter sounds:
s a t p i n m d g o c k ck
e u r h b f l ff ss

For more activities, free eBooks and practical advice to help your child progress with reading visit **oxfordowl.co.uk**

Chip's Letter Sounds

Written by Kate Ruttle and Annemarie Young
Illustrated by Nick Schon, based on original characters
created by Roderick Hunt and Alex Brychta

OXFORD

UNIVERSITY PRESS

Trace the letters.
Say the sound.

sun, sea, sand, sandwiches, socks, sandals, spade,
seagulls, sandcastle, straw, sails

Look for ten things in this picture that begin with **s**.

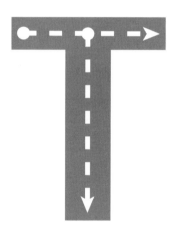

table, teapot, tray, towels, tent, train, tools, tractor, tennis racket/ball, tail

Look for ten things in this picture that begin with **t**.

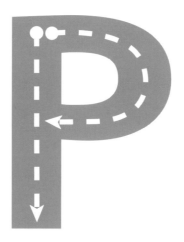

presents, paints, picture, penguins, parrot, panda,
polar bear, pop, pin, parents, pen

Point to all the things at my party that begin with **p**.

Say the sounds and then say the words.

s i t   p a t

ill, ink, insects, apple, ambulance, ant, animals,
bat, fan, hat, man, lamp, pat, rat, cat, fin, pillow

What things can you find in the picture that begin with **a** or **i**? Can you find anything with **a** or **i** in the middle of the word?

Say the sounds and then say the words.

m a n   p i n   n e t

night, necklace, newspaper, needle, net, moon,
Mum, mug, mice, monster, monkeys

Say the sounds and then say the words.

d o g   D a d   g a p

game, garden, green, girl, grass, goal, goldfish,
Dad, dinosaur, doll, dog, octopus, oranges

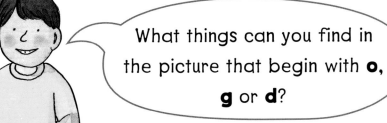

What things can you find in the picture that begin with **o**, **g** or **d**?

c C

k K

e E

Say the sounds and then say the words.

p a n   m o p

e gg   s o ck

cake, cook, caterpillar, competition, cat, car, castle, crown,
cream, crocodile, cup, kangaroo, kitchen, eggs, elephant

Dad and I have entered a cooking competition. How many things can you find in the picture that begin with **c, k** or **e**?

Say the sounds and then say the words.

h o p   m u g
r u b   r o ck

umbrella, rain, red, rabbit, river, rocks, holiday, head, hat, house,
horse, hop, hair, house, hug, rub, Mum, mug, tree trunk

How many things can you find in the picture that begin with **u, r** or **h**? Can you find anything with **u** in the middle of the word?

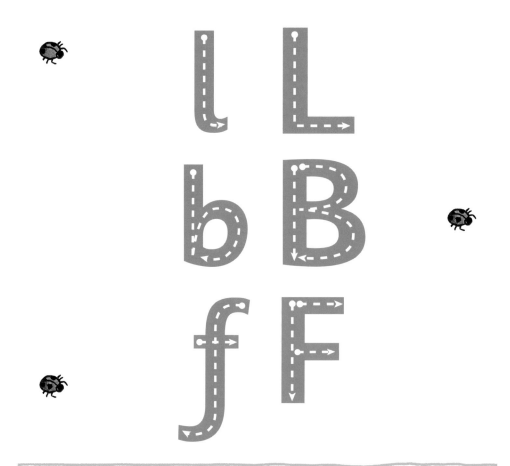

l L
b B
f F

Say the sounds and then say the words.

l e g   b i n
B i ff   m e ss

lady, lolly, leaf, litter, ladybird, flower, bee, butterfly, bench,
bin, biscuit, baby, buggy, balloon, bag, buildings

20

What things can you find in the picture that begin with **l**, **b** or **f**?

Tangled lines

Follow the lines to find the objects.

OXFORD
UNIVERSITY PRESS

Great Clarendon Street, Oxford OX2 6DP

Oxford University Press is a department of the University of Oxford.
It furthers the University's objective of excellence in research, scholarship,
and education by publishing worldwide. Oxford is a registered trade mark
of Oxford University Press in the UK and in certain other countries

Text © Annemarie Young and Kate Ruttle 2011
Illustrations © Alex Brychta and Nick Schon 2011

First published 2011. This edition published 2020.

Series Editors: Kate Ruttle, Annemarie Young

British Library Cataloguing in Publication Data available

ISBN: 978-0-19-277392-0

10 9 8 7 6 5 4 3 2

Printed in China

The characters in this work are the original creation
of Roderick Hunt and Alex Brychta who retain copyright
in the characters.

Paper used in the production of this book is a natural,
recyclable product made from wood grown in sustainable forests.
The manufacturing process conforms to the environmental
regulations of the country of origin.

Chip's Letter Sounds is a **Read with Oxford Stage 1** book for children who are taking their first steps in reading. If your child enjoyed this book, there are many more titles available at **Stage 1** to build their reading skills:

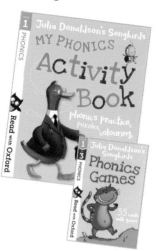

The next step, **Read with Oxford Stage 2**, helps your child develop early reading skills. Here are just a few to get you started:

To see the whole **Read with Oxford** range and to learn more about the **Read with Oxford Stages**, have a look at **oxfordowl.co.uk**. You'll also find practical advice, free eBooks and fun activities to get your child off to a flying start!

Read with Oxford

Welcome to Read with Oxford

Featuring much-loved characters, great authors, engaging storylines and fun activities, **Read with Oxford** offers an exciting range of carefully levelled reading books to build your child's reading confidence.

From the very first steps in phonics all the way to reading independence, our unique and simple levelling system – **Read with Oxford Stages** – will guide you to choose the right book for your child.

For more information about **Read with Oxford Stages** and the whole range go to **oxfordowl.co.uk**. You'll also find lots of useful advice, free eBooks and activities to support your child through their learning journey.

Helping your child with phonics

Phonics is a way of teaching reading that is used in Primary schools. Children are taught to read letters or groups of letters by saying the sound(s) they represent; so they are taught the letter 'm' sounds like 'mmm' when we say it. Children are then taught more sounds, and learn to blend them to read words.

This book is part of the comprehensive and trusted range of support for learning at home from Oxford University Press.

You will find more advice and resources to support your child's learning on Oxford Owl.
www.oxfordowl.co.uk

Read with Oxford   Progress with Oxford   Bond – exam preparation   Dictionaries

Tips for reading *Floppy's Fun Phonics*

Children learn best when reading is relaxed and enjoyable.

- Tell your child they are going to play a different game of 'I spy'.
- On each page, read the instruction aloud, then ask your child to read the captions and sentences on the left hand pages and try to match them to the pictures on the right.
- Encourage your child to sound out the letters and say the words (e.g. *l-i-d lid*).
- Give them lots of praise.
- Do the odd one out activity on every left hand page and the spot the difference activity on page 22.

Have fun!

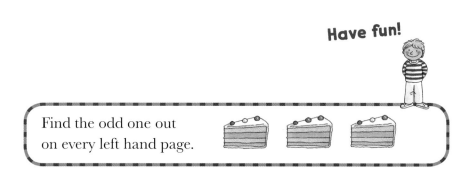

Find the odd one out
on every left hand page.

This book practices these letter sounds:

s a t p i n m d g o c c k e u r h b f ff ll

For more activities, free eBooks and practical advice to help your child progress with reading visit **oxfordowl.co.uk**

Floppy's Fun Phonics

Written by Kate Ruttle and Annemarie Young
Illustrated by Nick Schon, based on the original characters
created by Roderick Hunt and Alex Brychta

OXFORD
UNIVERSITY PRESS

Read the sentence on this card. Which picture matches the card?

Dad is sad.

Read the captions on these cards. Which card matches the picture?

rats on a sack

cats on a sock

6

Read the captions on these cards. Which card matches the picture?

a hen and
a bug

a hat on
a dog

8

Read the sentences on these cards. Which card matches the picture?

Run in the sun.

Sit in the sun.

Read the sentences on these cards. Which card matches the picture?

A dog can sit.

A dog can run.

Read the sentences on these cards. Can you match each card to its picture?

A dog is a pet.

The dog is wet.

Read the sentences on these cards. Can you match each card to its picture?

Run and hop.

Run to the top.

16

17

Read the sentences on these cards. Can you match each card to its picture?

Biff is on a mug.

It is a big red bug.

Read the sentences on these cards. Can you match each card to its picture?

Biff is in a sack.

A doll is in a backpack.

20

Spot the difference

Find the five differences in the two pictures of Floppy.

UNIVERSITY PRESS

Great Clarendon Street, Oxford OX2 6DP

Oxford University Press is a department of the University of Oxford.
It furthers the University's objective of excellence in research, scholarship,
and education by publishing worldwide. Oxford is a registered trade mark
of Oxford University Press in the UK and in certain other countries

Text © Roderick Hunt 2006
Illustrations © Alex Brychta 2006

First published 2006. This edition published 2020.

Series Editors: Kate Ruttle, Annemarie Young

British Library Cataloguing in Publication Data available

ISBN: 978-0-19-277394-4

10 9 8 7 6 5 4 3 2

Printed in China

Floppy's Fun Phonics is a **Read with Oxford Stage 1** book for children who are taking their first steps in reading. If your child enjoyed this book, there are many more titles available at **Stage 1** to build their reading skills:

The next step, **Read with Oxford Stage 2**, helps your child develop early reading skills. Here are just a few to get you started:

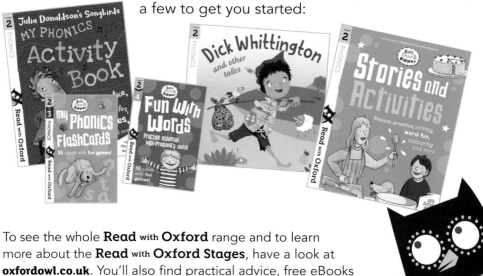

To see the whole **Read with Oxford** range and to learn more about the **Read with Oxford Stages**, have a look at **oxfordowl.co.uk**. You'll also find practical advice, free eBooks and fun activities to get your child off to a flying start!

Welcome to Read with Oxford

Featuring much-loved characters, great authors, engaging storylines and fun activities, **Read with Oxford** offers an exciting range of carefully levelled reading books to build your child's reading confidence.

From the very first steps in phonics all the way to reading independence, our unique and simple levelling system – **Read with Oxford Stages** – will guide you to choose the right book for your child.

For more information about **Read with Oxford Stages** and the whole range go to **oxfordowl.co.uk**. You'll also find lots of useful advice, free eBooks and activities to support your child through their learning journey.

Helping your child with phonics

Phonics is a way of teaching reading that is used in Primary schools. Children are taught to read letters or groups of letters by saying the sound(s) they represent; so they are taught the letter 'm' sounds like 'mmm' when we say it. Children are then taught more sounds, and learn to blend them to read words.

This book is part of the comprehensive and trusted range of support for learning at home from Oxford University Press.

You will find more advice and resources to support your child's learning on Oxford Owl.
www.oxfordowl.co.uk

Read with Oxford   Progress with Oxford   Bond – exam preparation   Dictionaries

Tips for reading *Kipper's Alphabet I Spy*

Children learn best when reading is relaxed
and enjoyable.

- Tell your child they are going to help Kipper play 'I spy'.

- For each left hand page, introduce the alphabet letter by
  saying its sound clearly, for example, make the sound of 'b'
  as in *bat*. Don't say 'bee' or 'buh'.

- Ask your child to trace the letter with their fingers while
  repeating the letter sound.

- Then ask them to 'spy' objects on the opposite page starting
  with the letter.

- Ask them to say what the objects are, and repeat the word
  slowly, emphasising the sound of the initial letter.

- Give lots of praise as your child plays the game with you.

- Do the animal tracks puzzle on every
  page and the maze on page 22.

Have fun!

Match the animal tracks on each left hand page
to one of the creatures on the right hand page.

This book introduces the letters and
sounds of the alphabet:
a b c d e f g h i j k l m n o p
q r s t u v w x y z

For more activities, free eBooks
and practical advice to help
your child progress with reading
visit **oxfordowl.co.uk**

Kipper's Alphabet I Spy

Written by Kate Ruttle and Annemarie Young,
based on original characters created by Roderick Hunt and Alex Brychta
Illustrated by Alex Brychta

UNIVERSITY PRESS

I spy with my little eye, something beginning with...

apple, ant, Biff, banana, ball, cat, candle

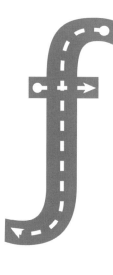

dinosaur, duck, egg, elephant, Floppy, feather

g

h

i

goose, goat, gate, hair, hat, horse, insect

9

jelly, jigsaw, Kipper, key, kangaroo, ladybird, lion

10

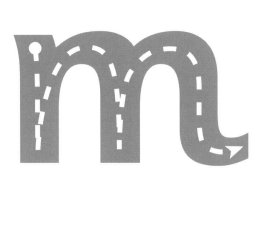

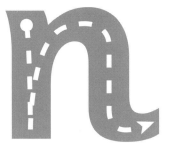

moon, monkey, milk, nose, nail, net

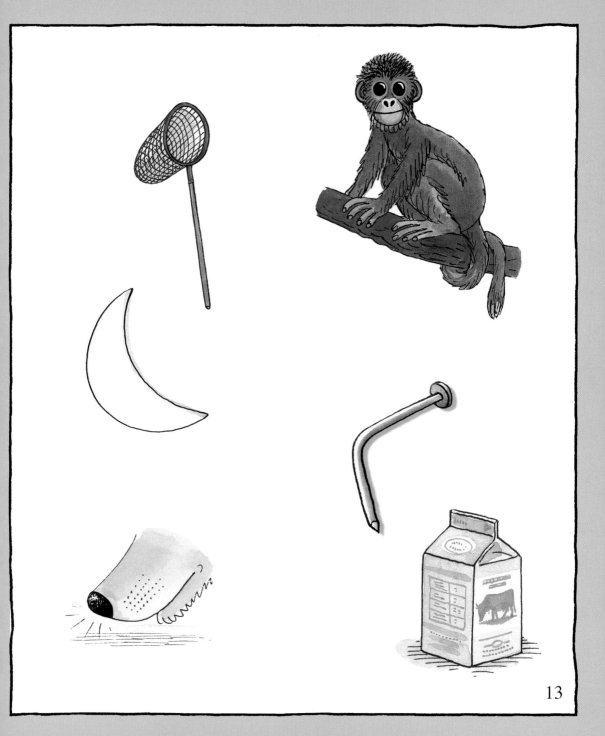

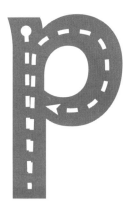

orange, octopus, pear, penguin, purple, queen, quilt

red, rabbit, rainbow, sandwich, sun, tiger, teddy, t-shirt

umbrella, under, volcano, violin, watermelon, watch

18

fox, box, yellow, yo-yo, yawn, zebra, zigzag

20

A maze

Help Kipper get to Floppy.

OXFORD
UNIVERSITY PRESS

Great Clarendon Street, Oxford OX2 6DP

Oxford University Press is a department of the University of Oxford.
It furthers the University's objective of excellence in research, scholarship,
and education by publishing worldwide. Oxford is a registered trade mark
of Oxford University Press in the UK and in certain other countries

First published 2011. This edition published 2020.

Series Editors: Kate Ruttle, Annemarie Young

British Library Cataloguing in Publication Data available

ISBN: 978-0-19-277397-5

10 9 8 7 6 5 4 3 2

Printed in China

Paper used in the production of this book is a natural,
recyclable product made from wood grown in sustainable forests.
The manufacturing process conforms to the environmental
regulations of the country of origin.

Kipper's Alphabet I Spy is a **Read** with **Oxford Stage 1** book for children who are taking their first steps in reading. If your child enjoyed this book, there are many more titles available at **Stage 1** to build their reading skills:

The next step, **Read** with **Oxford Stage 2**, helps your child develop early reading skills. Here are just a few to get you started:

To see the whole **Read** with **Oxford** range and to learn more about the **Read** with **Oxford Stages**, have a look at **oxfordowl.co.uk**. You'll also find practical advice, free eBooks and fun activities to get your child off to a flying start!

Read with **Oxford**

Welcome to Read with Oxford

Featuring much-loved characters, great authors, engaging storylines and fun activities, **Read with Oxford** offers an exciting range of carefully levelled reading books to build your child's reading confidence.

From the very first steps in phonics all the way to reading independence, our unique and simple levelling system – **Read with Oxford Stages** – will guide you to choose the right book for your child.

For more information about **Read with Oxford Stages** and the whole range go to **oxfordowl.co.uk**. You'll also find lots of useful advice, free eBooks and activities to support your child through their learning journey.

Helping your child with phonics

Phonics is a way of teaching reading that is used in Primary schools. Children are taught to read letters or groups of letters by saying the sound(s) they represent; so they are taught the letter 'm' sounds like 'mmm' when we say it. Children are then taught more sounds, and learn to blend them to read words.

This book is part of the comprehensive and trusted range of support for learning at home from Oxford University Press.

You will find more advice and resources to support your child's learning on Oxford Owl. **www.oxfordowl.co.uk**

Read with Oxford   **Progress with Oxford**   **Bond – exam preparation**   **Dictionaries**

Tips for reading *Cat in a Bag*

This book has two stories: *Cat in a Bag* (page 3) and *It* (page 17).

- Talk about the title and the picture on the front cover and title pages of each story.
- Find the letters *a* and *i* in these titles and talk about the sounds they make when you read them in these words.
- Look at the *a*, *i* and *u* words on pages 4 and 18. Say the sounds in each word and then say each word (e.g. *t-i-n, tin*).
- Read the stories together and find the words with *a*, *i*, *o* and *u*.
- Do the fun activities at the end of each story.

Children enjoy re-reading stories and this helps to build their confidence.

Have fun!

After you have read *It*, find five birds in the pictures.

The main sounds practised in this book are 'a' as in *bag*, 'i' as in *tin*, and 'u' as in *tub*.

For more activities, free eBooks and practical advice to help your child progress with reading visit **oxfordowl.co.uk**

Cat in a Bag

Written by Roderick Hunt
Illustrated by Nick Schon,
based on the original characters
created by Roderick Hunt and Alex Brychta

OXFORD
UNIVERSITY PRESS

Read these words

in	cat
bag	tin
hat	had
tub	tap

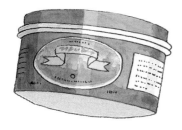

Wilf had a cat.

He put a hat on the cat.

Wilf had a bag.

He put the cat in the bag.

tap, tap, tap

7

Wilf had a tub.

He put the bag in the tub.

tap, tap, tap

Wilf had a tin.

He put the tub in the tin.

tap, tap, tap

11

Wilf had the cat in his hat.

Talk about the story

What did Wilf put on the cat?

Why was Wilf dressed up?

How did the cat get on top of Wilf's head?

What magic trick would you like to do?

Missing letters

Choose the letter to make the word.

c_t

W_lf

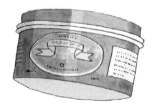

t_n

h_t

What's in the picture?

Match the words to things you can find in the picture.
Point to the ones you can find.

Wilf   tub   bag

tin   cat   hat

It

Written by Roderick Hunt
Illustrated by Nick Schon,
based on the original characters
created by Roderick Hunt and Alex Brychta

OXFORD
UNIVERSITY PRESS

Read these words

him   Mum

hit   rug

fit   but

did   mud

Chip put on the cap.
He was 'it'.

Mum ran and Kipper ran.

Mum got on the box.

Kipper got on the rug.

Biff ran.

She got on the box.

Dad ran, but Chip got him.

Dad put on the cap.
It did not fit.

Bam! Dad ran into Floppy.

Dad hit the mud.

Talk about the story

What game was the family playing?

Which people were 'it'?

Why did Dad call Floppy a 'Bad dog'?

What games do you like to play?

27

Missing letters

Choose the letter to make the word.

b__x

r__g

m__d

l__g

What's in the picture?

Match the words to things you can find in the picture.

Point to the ones you can find.

box   on   dog   mud

Mum   log   rug   run

Word search

How many words can you find with *a*, *o*, *i* or *u* in them?
Can you write them down?

c	a	t	i	n
o	r	u	g	u
p	i	l	o	g
b	o	x	i	p
t	a	h	i	m

OXFORD

UNIVERSITY PRESS

Great Clarendon Street, Oxford OX2 6DP

Oxford University Press is a department of the University of Oxford.
It furthers the University's objective of excellence in research, scholarship,
and education by publishing worldwide. Oxford is a registered trade mark
of Oxford University Press in the UK and in certain other countries

Text © Roderick Hunt 2007
Illustrations © Alex Brychta and Nick Schon 2007

First published 2007. This edition published 2020.

Series Editors: Kate Ruttle, Annemarie Young

British Library Cataloguing in Publication Data available

ISBN: 978-0-19-277391-3

10 9 8 7 6 5 4 3 2

Printed in China

Cat in a Bag is a **Read** with **Oxford Stage 1** book for children who are taking their first steps in reading. If your child enjoyed this book, there are many more titles available at **Stage 1** to build their reading skills:

The next step, **Read** with **Oxford Stage 2**, helps your child develop early reading skills. Here are just a few to get you started:

To see the whole **Read** with **Oxford** range and to learn more about the **Read** with **Oxford Stages**, have a look at **oxfordowl.co.uk**. You'll also find practical advice, free eBooks and fun activities to get your child off to a flying start!

Read with Oxford

Welcome to Read with Oxford

Featuring much-loved characters, great authors, engaging storylines and fun activities, **Read with Oxford** offers an exciting range of carefully levelled reading books to build your child's reading confidence.

From the very first steps in phonics all the way to reading independence, our unique and simple levelling system – **Read with Oxford Stages** – will guide you to choose the right book for your child.

For more information about **Read with Oxford Stages** and the whole range go to **oxfordowl.co.uk**. You'll also find lots of useful advice, free eBooks and activities to support your child through their learning journey.

Stories for wider reading

This story uses simple everyday language. Encourage your child to read as much as they can with you. You can help your child to read any longer words in the context of the story. Children enjoy re-reading stories and this helps to build their confidence and their vocabulary.

This book is part of the comprehensive and trusted range of support for learning at home from Oxford University Press.

You will find more advice and resources to support your child's learning on Oxford Owl. **www.oxfordowl.co.uk**

Read with Oxford   **Progress with Oxford**   **Bond – exam preparation**   **Dictionaries**

Tips for reading *Mum's New Hat*

Children learn best when reading is relaxed and enjoyable.

- Talk about the title and the picture on the front cover.

- Look through the pictures so your child can see what the story is about.

- Read the story to your child, placing your finger under each word as you read.

- Read the story again and encourage your child to join in.

- Give lots of praise as your child reads with you.

- Talk about the story.

- Do the fun activity on page 22.

Have fun!

After you have read the story, find the feather hidden in every picture.

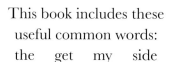

This book includes these useful common words:
the   get   my   side

For more activities, free eBooks and practical advice to help your child progress with reading visit **oxfordowl.co.uk**

Mum's New Hat

Written by Roderick Hunt
Illustrated by Alex Brychta

OXFORD

UNIVERSITY PRESS

Mum had a new hat.

The wind blew.

It blew Mum's hat off.

"Get my hat," said Mum.

Dad ran.

The wind blew.

Oh no!

"Get that hat," said Dad.

Kipper ran.

The wind blew.

Oh no!

"Get that hat," said Kipper.

Biff ran.

The wind blew.

Oh no!

"Look at my new hat!"
said Mum.

Talk about the story

How did Mum lose her new hat?

Why do you think Biff has a camera?

What funny things happened to Mum's hat?

Have any funny things happened to you on windy days?

21

A maze

Help Mum get her hat.

OXFORD
UNIVERSITY PRESS

Great Clarendon Street, Oxford OX2 6DP

Oxford University Press is a department of the University of Oxford.
It furthers the University's objective of excellence in research, scholarship,
and education by publishing worldwide. Oxford is a registered trade mark
of Oxford University Press in the UK and in certain other countries

Text © Roderick Hunt 2006
Illustrations © Alex Brychta 2006

First published 2006. This edition published 2020.

Series Editors: Kate Ruttle, Annemarie Young

British Library Cataloguing in Publication Data available

ISBN: 978-0-19-277406-4

10 9 8 7 6 5 4 3 2

Printed in China

Paper used in the production of this book is a natural,
recyclable product made from wood grown in sustainable forests.
The manufacturing process conforms to the environmental
regulations of the country of origin.

Mum's New Hat is a **Read** with **Oxford Stage 1** book for children who are taking their first steps in reading. If your child enjoyed this book, there are many more titles available at **Stage 1** to build their reading skills:

The next step, **Read** with **Oxford Stage 2**, helps your child develop early reading skills. Here are just a few to get you started:

To see the whole **Read** with **Oxford** range and to learn more about the **Read** with **Oxford Stages**, have a look at oxfordowl.co.uk. You'll also find practical advice, free eBooks and fun activities to get your child off to a flying start!

Read with **Oxford**